Hatching and rec
your birds

D1646100

ncubation is the natural or artificial hatching of eggs. You can use the natural way – that is, let the birds sit and hatch their own offspring – or you can use the alternative, which is to opt for the artificial method and use an incubator.

Whichever method you choose to use, incubation is one of the most frustrating and yet pleasurable things to do. There is no way of telling what the results will be, there will be times when you have a great hatch and most of the eggs are fertile but there will also be the times when the results are so bad you wonder what you have done wrong.

Using a broody hen is always the simplest way of hatching and brooding your chicks, but this gives you a limited amount of chicks because the hen can only hatch so many at one time. With the incubator you have control over how many eggs you can set to hatch and also you can add to the eggs at various dates during the incubation period. This also allows you to candle your eggs and, if the fertility is bad, then you can add more eggs to try and ensure a better result.

During the incubation period you must remember to keep good records. It is very important for you to have the correct information as to when the eggs are due to hatch, and if you have added eggs at a later stage then it is even more crucial to keep records which tell you when eggs are ready to be candled, and also when the second batch was added in order to calculate their hatch date.

Whether you are following the natural or artifical hatching route, hatching and rearing problems come in a wide variation that we cover in the following pages. It's true that many can be rectified or avoided, but it's best to understand that some of the others causes are totally out of our control!

Terry Beebe

Published by
KELSEY PUBLISHING LTD

Printed by TCA Print Solutions on behalf of
Kelsey Publishing Ltd, Cudham Tithe Barn, Berry's Hill, Cudham, Kent TN16 3AG
Tel: 01959 541444 *Fax:* 01959 541400 *Email:* kelseybooks@kelsey.co.uk *Website:* www.kelsey.co.uk

©2010 **ISBN: 978 1 907426 07 0**

Hatching and rearing your birds

CONTENTS

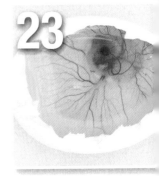

Nature v incubator

Chris Graham offers some practical advice on how to get the best from your eggs

For many keepers, incubator hatching is the most practical option – but is it the best? After all, hens have been hatching their own eggs for thousands of years, so they know a thing or two about getting it right! Incubators, on the other hand, attempt to emulate the hen's natural and instinctive performance in a mechanical way.

These machines can work brilliantly, but they can also be very disappointing in the hands of inexperienced operators. The 'fiddle factor' tends to be many users' downfall – they just can't leave the machine alone to do its job. Repeated opening of the lid and needless adjustment of the controls can send the success rate plummeting.

While state-of-the-art machines are completely automatic, the danger is that this can lead to complacency and an over-reliance on technology. It's vital to have a good understanding of the whole hatching process, but buying a machine that offers to do it all for you tends to take away the need for that understanding.

Natural hatching certainly involves more work for the keeper, and requires good poultry management if space is limited. But if you only want to hatch a few birds, and have a reliable, broody breed to work with (Orpington, Silkie, Sussex), then it can be a reliable method of producing what many consider to be stronger, superior chicks.

Heat and moisture

One of the potential problems associated with using an incubator is that you're totally dependent on its ability to effectively manage the three vital factors; heat, humidity and egg turning. Each of these variable factors can have a very damaging effect on hatching potential if it's allowed to slip out of tolerance.

Inadequate turning can cause the developing yolk to stick to the inside of the shell, insufficient temperature can halt embryo development completely and poor humidity control can cause death in the shell. Humidity that's too high can prevent the egg from losing necessary moisture through evaporation, meaning that the chick can drown before it hatches, while levels that are set too low tend to dry out, toughen and shrink the membrane inside the shell, preventing the chick from turning as it needs to, and halting the hatching process.

If using an incubator, be sure to

read the instructions carefully and to follow them exactly. Also take care to site it in an appropriate environment (out of direct sunlight and avoiding temperature/humidity extremes). Finally, note that egg turning must stop for the final three days of incubation.

Fertility levels

Overall egg quality is at the root of hatching success, but is something that many enthusiasts fail to appreciate. Poor hatch rates are often blamed on some problem with the incubator when, in fact, the eggs weren't fertile in the first place.

To give yourself the best chance of success, avoid incubating eggs that are misshapen, or show obviously poor shell quality or are more than a week old. Also, try to ensure they've been produced by young, healthy parents.

Eggs bought by mail order (from specialist suppliers or via the Internet) are inevitably something of a gamble. Their provenance and real age are both potential concerns, as are the way they are packaged and transported. For the best results, take the trouble to visit the supplier (recommended to you by the relevant breed club) and collect the eggs yourself.

Of course, you can't actually check on fertility levels until about day 10 of the incubation process, when eggs can be 'candled' (viewed using a bright back-light to silhouette the contents) to check visually for embryo development. If you see a spidery pattern of blood vessels then there's life in there!

Times and temps

Under ideal conditions the total time between setting an egg and the chick hatching varies slightly across the domestic poultry species. Chickens typically take 21 days, while most ducks add another week to this time, at 28 days (Muscovies can take about 35 days).

Turkeys also tend to hatch at the 28-day mark, as do Guinea fowl and Pheasants, but Peafowl are slightly slower, usually emerging after about 30 days.

Chickens, ducks, Guinea fowl and Pheasants all require the incubator to be maintained at 37.7°C (100°F), but turkeys and geese need it very slightly cooler, at

37.5°C (99°F). There's more variation with humidity which, for chickens, should be 35-40% for the first 18 days, then increased to 60-65% for the final three. Turkeys, ducks and Guinea fowl need much about the same, but geese require a slightly higher level over the day 1-18 period.

Helping hand?

Hatching doesn't always run exactly to plan. Sometimes chicks can take a little longer than expected to emerge and, sadly, sometimes they just never get out at all. The question of whether or not to intervene – known as 'assisted hatching' – is a tricky one.

Experienced breeders tend to take the view that if the chick cannot extricate itself from the shell unaided, then it's not worth

While 'assisted hatching' may not be to everyone's taste, it can be worth a go if you want to give a struggling chick everychance of survival

having anyway. The belief is that the failure to get out is indicative of an underlying weakness of some sort that, ultimately, will result in the bird growing into a poor specimen.

Those of a more sensitive nature, however, are more inclined to do what they can to save the young bird, and if that means helping it out of its shell then so be it. Gentleness is the key. If the chick has managed to 'pip' (broken through the shell, with its 'beak tooth'), then use tweezers to carefully lift away small pieces of the shell. If you see red blood vessels in the membrane beneath the shell then the chick isn't fully

developed and you should wait before proceeding.

In some respects this is a game of patience while, in others, it's a race against time. There's no guarantee of success, or that the chick will survive if you manage to get it out. But many keepers simply feel happier that they've made an effort to save the bird's life.

Time to dry

It's very important that, after hatching (which can take anything up to 12 hours), the chicks are kept in the warm incubator for a further 24 hours so that they have plenty of time to recover from the ordeal of hatching, and to dry out completely before being moved to the brooder.

This stage is very important as newly-hatched chicks are all too easily chilled, which is something to be avoided. The youngsters won't need to be fed at this stage as they have internal reserves of food (from the yolk) sufficient to last them about two days.

Any eggs which remain unhatched for longer than about three days after their due date – and show no signs of life – should be disposed of.

Chick problems

Regrettably, not all chicks turn out to be perfect, cute little bundles of fluff. Things can and do go wrong during their development, and problems can occur in the first few hours after hatching that need to be dealt with.

Developmental trouble – be it caused by some sort of infection, poor environment or a genetic defect – will have serious consequences for the chick. Either it'll die during the incubation period (or during hatching), or it'll emerge with an obvious deformity such as missing or twisted limbs. In these cases you have to make a responsible judgement call about quality of life…

The delicate nature of young chicks, and in particular, the softness of their bones and muscles, means that they are prone to slipping and dislocations. So incubator egg trays which are too smooth are a common cause of an unpleasant condition called 'splayed' or 'spraddled' leg.

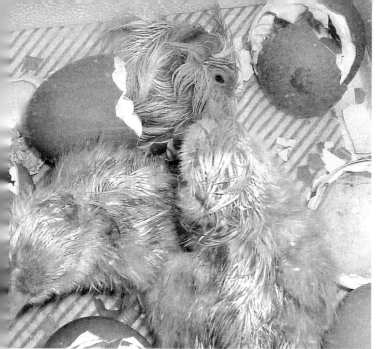

Note the cloth on the floor of this incubator, intended to give the newly-hatched chicks important grip as they stand and begin walking for the first time.

The chicks literally slip and do the splits, which leaves them with legs fixed at odd and unnatural angles. Putting this right means gently working the legs back into the correct position, then using a small figure-of-eight of string or rubber band to hold them together until the muscles are sufficiently strengthened. With great care, most chicks can be nursed through this condition.

Moving on

Once your new chicks have recovered from hatching, and are thoroughly dry and fluffed-up, then they need to be moved into a larger space to begin the 'brooding' stage of their early development.

The birds are particularly vulnerable to both low temperature and disease at this time, so great care is needed as they are moved from the 'security' of the incubator. If their new home is too cold they'll be reluctant to start eating and drinking, and will quickly become dehydrated.

They will require a safe environment offering warmth, protection from draughts, food and water. If you have just a handful of chicks then a stout, large cardboard box with a good layer of clean,

fresh shavings on the floor and a 60W light bulb suspended above to provide heat should be OK.

It's vital that the heat source is sufficient to prevent the chicks getting chilled – placing the brooder box in a warmer rather than a cooler environment will help with this. Their behaviour is a good guide to their condition. If they all huddle immediately below the heat source, they're too cold. If they're reluctant to go near the heat source, then they're probably too hot.

Happy brooder chicks will be constantly moving and making a 'chip, chip' sound. Long, drawn-out cheeping is a sign of distress.

First feed

It's very important to get the chicks eating and drinking as soon as possible, once they're in the brooder. Chick crumb and clean, fresh water must be made available from the start, and you can help encourage eating by adding a little finely chopped hard-boiled egg or spring onion.

Place the food and drink in very shallow dishes around the edge of the brooder area; never directly under the heat source. Be methodical about changing the water every day and cleaning the

dishes to prevent the build-up of slime.

Young chicks must be encouraged to drink; it's more important than feeding at this stage. Young chicks can lose significant amounts of body fat and weight, but still survive. However, if just 10% of their body moisture content is lost, then death will be imminent.

Add a little fine grit (sprinkled into the feed) after the first week to aid the development of their digestive systems, and then repeat this every two weeks until the birds are six weeks old. At this point, start adding 'growers' grit. Feed chick crumb for the first eight weeks, then switch to growers pellets or mash.

Warm enough?

Correct temperature control is essential as the chicks are growing their first feathers. Bigger brooder units will require a specialist heat source. Infrared bulbs are popular, producing either red or white light. Some breeders, though, prefer 'dull emitters' which produce heat, but no light.

Too much light for chicks can be a problem, causing accelerated development, nervousness and vices such as feather-pecking. Ideally, chicks should live in a conventional day/night light cycle (10-12 hours of light), provided by a dull emitter/ separate light source combination.

The temperature under the heat source is best maintained at 34°C (93°F). Seek the advice of your supplier if using a specialist heat source, about how best to establish this. Also, make sure the brooder is warmed-up properly before the birds are first introduced.

The heat source will need to be adjustable, so that levels can be reduced as the brooding period progresses. In most instances this is done simply by raising the unit; suspending it on a chain will make this much simpler. As a guide, start it at about 16-18in (40-45cm) above the floor – checking the temperature with a thermometer – and raise it a little every seven days, for the first five or six weeks. After this, the birds will have their first set of feathers, and will be better able to regulate their own body temperature. •

How to hatch

It's vital that your incubator – whatever type – is thoroughly cleaned before and after use; if not, it'll quickly become a haven for bacteria.

If you are planning to buy an incubator to hatch you own chicks, Terry Beebe outlines the practical basics

Incubation has always been a subject that seems to cause problems and disappointment for many poultry fanciers, both new and old. Beginners tend to get a bit confused by all that's involved and often find it difficult to get to the bottom of how best to hatch eggs in this way.

There are so many basic questions to be asked and answered and we know that many beginners find it hard to unearth the specific information they need. So here we'll cover those basics in what we hope is a clear and straightforward manner!

The blame game

The first thing to appreciate is that ultimate success with an incubator can never be guaranteed, particularly using those aimed at the domestic end of the market. You must expect failures, and shouldn't get too downcast when they occur.

Typically, people like to blame the incubator for their troubles but, in my experience, these machines are only as good as their operators – most problems stem from some sort of human error.

For those just starting out, it's important to choose an incubator that's both easy to understand and use. Thers is a great choice on the market these days, and it can be hard to decide exactly what to buy. As always, the best thing to do is

Hatching chicks is still a wondrous process, even for the experienced breeder.

How many eggs?

Egg capacity ranges from three right up to hundreds, but machines that can take 25-45 seem to be the most popular. Cost is another extremely variable factor. Size and specification are obvious determining factors, as is whether or not the unit is fan-assisted. The most basic incubators are fitted with a simple, thermostatically-controlled heat source – often a light bulb – and are classified as 'still air' units. The more refined approach is to fit a fan which ensures even temperature distribution throughout the interior (still air units can suffer with undesirable 'hot spots'). In my view, fan-assisted machines are the ones to go for, and you should expect to pay anything between £125 and £500 for a well-made example.

That said, many experienced breeders I know prefer to use a still air incubator as a hatcher because they find that the moving air in a fan-assisted unit can dry out the membrane inside the eggs, and actually prevents hatching. This illustrates the problem with incubation – so many variables and so many differing opinions! Based on my experiences, though, I definitely prefer moving air.

I'd always advise buying your incubator from a recognised specialist outlet. There are bargains to be had with secondhand units, and from buying on the Internet, but there are obvious risks attached too. Buying new at least means that you'll be getting a clean, impurity-free machine that should be complete and in full running order. You'll also have all the accessories – hatching trays, electrical cables, egg trays, thermometer – plus some degree of product support and a guarantee.

Next you must decide where you're going to put your new machine. Think carefully about this because the surrounding environment is a vital issue. While modern incubators (particularly the higher-spec machines) are pretty effective at maintaining the correct temperature inside, you still need to avoid exposing them to ambient temperature extremes. Ideally the unit should be sited in a dry, draught-proof area where the ambient temperature will remain

take advice from existing, experienced users; chicken keepers you already know, or experts from within a poultry breed club or local society. There's no substitute for unbiased, experience-based advice and recommendation.

You shouldn't need to spend a fortune either, although always remember that purchase price does generally reflect the machine's operating performance. Essentially, there are three main classifications of incubator; manual, semi-automatic and fully-automatic. Manual machines are exactly as they sound – a simple, heated compartment with racking to support a set number of eggs that'll have to be turned individually by hand. The semi-automatic alternative represents the next step up the sophistication ladder, and is certainly more convenient to live with. The eggs are turned with the aid of a lever, which rotates them all at the same time... but you still have to remember to do it, of course!

The fully-automatic machines do virtually everything for you. The eggs are turned by an electric motor on an hourly basis, which is great. These units represent the easiest option but, as you might expect, they are the most expensive too. However, an added advantage is that this level of machine can

normally double-up as a hatcher too, once the turning motor has been disconnected.

The egg capacity of the incubator is another very important factor. It's crucial to match this to your needs and your facilities. Remember that it's all too easy to get drawn into hatching too many chicks which you'll then have to look after. There's also the potential problem of male birds to consider. On average, the male/female split will be 50:50, so the more you hatch the more males you'll have on your hands.

Small incubators tend to be blamed when things go wrong. They are less sophisticated than the expensive machines, certainly, but they also tend to be used by inexperienced enthusiasts who make mistakes.

just about constant, day and night. Direct sunlight and freezing conditions should be avoided, as should centrally-heated rooms and those that are in constant use.

Set the temperature to 37.8°C, and run the machine for at least 24 hours to make sure everything is operating smoothly and reliably – check regularly that the set temperature is being maintained (fluctuation of a degree or so either way is OK, but no more than this). Most modern machines are very effective at temperature regulation, and some are supplied pre-set by the manufacturer so there's no setting required.

Safe storage

The next step is to collect the eggs. These should be as fresh as possible and, if you're buying them from a breeder, then it's important that they are allowed a few hours to settle after the journey/delivery before being put into the incubator. Egg storage is another aspect which many beginners are unsure about. I'm frequently asked how best to look after collected eggs prior to them being 'set' in the machine. Well, what you have to remember is that each day that passes causes an egg to lose a percentage of its fertility, so the sooner they are set into the unit the better the chances of a good result.

When storing the eggs you'll need to keep them away from temperature extremes (out of direct sunlight, and not in the

Higher-spec incubators offer automatic egg turning and fan-assistance. They are easier to use, but a good deal more expensive to buy.

fridge). I keep mine in an egg tray – pointed end facing down – that sits in the incubator room. I also set this tray at a slight angle, and alter this from side to side once a day to prevent the embryos from sticking to the inside of the shell. This movement need only be minimal, but it's very important.

Finally, before setting the eggs in the incubator, they'll need to be cleaned. Do this gently; scrape off any heavy dirt, then use a specialist egg wash product to clean the whole shell thoroughly. The objective is to remove/kill any bacterial growth that may have established itself on the surface. The warm, damp environment inside the incubator provides ideal

growth conditions for these nasties, so you need to remove them before you get started.

Setting the eggs is normally a straightforward process and, depending on the type of machine being used, they'll either lay on their sides, or be supported upright (pointed end downwards). Chicken eggs then remain inside for 21 days but, during this time, you'll need to check the them for fertility using a process called 'candling'. A bright light is used from behind to highlight the contents of the egg; the developing embryo is clearly visible inside. In this way, infertile eggs can be removed, which is important as they pose a potential health risk to the other fertile eggs.

INCUBATOR BASICS

- Set the incubator to the correct temperature, 37.8°C, and test run it for 24 hours before setting any eggs.
- If the hatching eggs have travelled or have been moved any distance, rest in one position for a few hours/overnight.
- Clean the eggs thoroughly using a specialist product. Make sure the incubator itself is clean too.
- Carefully set the eggs in the incubator.
- Don't add water to the incubator for the first 15 days.
- Ensure that the eggs are being turned correctly, and frequently enough, and check the temperature regularly.
- 'Candle' the eggs during the early part of incubation – at around the 10-12-day mark – to check for fertility. Remove any which are infertile and clear.
- Add water to the incubator on day 15-17, and keep the level topped-up thereafter.

- Top-up the water for the final time on day 20, then leave the incubator closed until after hatching.
- If all goes to plan, the chicks should hatch on day 21, but always allow a day extra for any late ones. Any that are slower to hatch than this will likely have problems.
- After they've hatched, allow the chicks 24 hours in the warm incubator to dry out thoroughly and 'fluff-up'.
- Remove the chicks from the incubator on day 22-23, and transfer them to the brooder for rearing. Make sure their beaks are dipped in water to encourage them to drink.
- Sprinkle chick crumb from above, so that the noise sparks their interest, and starts them pecking. You may need to encourage them to eat by repeat sprinkling.
- Make sure that the heat level in the brooder is set at about the same as it was in the incubator. It's important that the chicks don't get too hot or too cold.

While you are collecting eggs for the incubator, they need to be stored securely, away from temperature extremes and at an alternating angle to prevent the embryo from sticking inside.

Hatching chicks is one of the most rewarding things I've ever done and, to this day, I'm still fascinated by the whole, amazing process. The first chicks you hatch are so special – I can still remember mine, and the marvellous feeling of achievement that came with them. There's something deeply satisfying about breeding, hatching and successfully rearing your own flock of chickens; it's something that everyone with the necessary facilities should try. There *will* be failures and all you can do is learn from them and move on.

Methodical approach

From day one I always make a point of checking regularly that everything in the unit is running smoothly; never take it for granted that all's well. Most modern incubators have a transparent cover or door window, which enables you to visually check the eggs without having to open the unit, which would lose precious heat and risk upsetting humidity levels.

Humidity is a big issue among incubator users, with many having problems getting the balance right. It can be difficult to control it effectively on the smaller, cheap-and-cheerful units, but the higher-specification machines nowadays offer very effective humidity regulation systems. Whatever type you use, though, humidity is an aspect which always requires consideration. However, it does seem to dominate as an issue for lots of users, which shouldn't be the case.

Life is certainly tougher at the 'entry level' end of the incubator scale, but I think that many problems with these machines are caused by the fact that, by and large, they are being used by very inexperienced enthusiasts. The secret is to follow the manufacturer's instructions to the letter, and to resist the temptation to keep opening the unit. Add the

This is what it's all about; a tray full of healthy chicks awaiting transfer to the brooder.

water as recommended and take advice from other users.

The 'Incubator Basics' panel I've included here summarises my approach to egg hatching. It's a method which I've established over many years of successful breeding. However, please bear in mind that the details can vary according to individual circumstances – such as incubator location, design and the type of eggs being hatched. So use the information as a general guide, and relate it to the instructions supplied with your own machine.

What you've got to remember is that using an incubator isn't rocket science! Follow the correct method, use good hatching eggs and work with a good level of common sense and you'll get the results you deserve. Also, don't forget that after *every* hatch the incubator will need to be cleaned and disinfected; the interior of these machines provides the ideal environment for germs and bacteria to develop and grow, so good hygiene is very important. There's a range of good incubator sanitises and cleaners generally available, so there's no excuse for encountering problems in this respect. Once again, instructions should be followed, and liquids must be kept off electrical components for obvious reasons. •

Good or bad eggs?

Dudley Mallett explains that there can be winners and losers on both sides when it comes to trading in hatching eggs

With the knock-on effects of the various Avian Influenza scares, the consequent dip in poultry shows yet the continued growth of the poultry-keeping hobby as a domestic pastime, we now find ourselves (at the time of writing) in a situation where there's a general shortage of chickens available for purchase.

Other factors, such as the increases in fuel prices which seem to have reduced the attendances at poultry shows a bit, and the lack of poultry markets, mean that increasing numbers of people are turning to DIY egg hatching at home.

Egg search

This is all well and good for those with a ready supply of quality hatching eggs, but for keepers without a cockerel at home who want to get into incubation for the first time, sourcing good, fertile eggs for 'setting' can be much more of a struggle. Clearly there are plenty of options when it comes to buying hatching eggs these days; many outlets are hobbyists in the Fancy, or small to medium-sized breeders. The breeds available are many and varied too, and customers are spoilt for choice with waterfowl, chickens and ornamental birds being available.

The biggest problem is locating a breeder who can supply the breed type and colour you are interested in. As in all things, the majority of egg suppliers are honest but, unfortunately, there seems to be a number who are not. There's a certain amount of 'jumping on the bandwagon' going on, as less scrupulous traders are riding the popularity of the hobby for all it's worth.

For this reason, my first piece of advice is always to deal with a reputable supplier who has been recommended to you by a breed club, your local poultry society or a fellow enthusiast with first-hand experience of the breeder and his or her birds. This really is the best way to proceed if you care about quality.

Of course, many people turn straight to the internet in search of poultry bargains, which is fine as long as you are cautious. The various online auction sites have hundreds of hatching eggs listed among their

Polystyrene trays like this are the best option when posting hatching eggs but, unfortunately, not even these can guarantee that the eggs will arrive at their destination in prime, incubatable condition.

NEVER FORGET THAT...

- No supplier can look at an intact hatching egg and tell that it's fertile.

- No supplier can guarantee his or her eggs are all fertile.

- The only way to check fertility is either to crack the egg on to a plate and view its germ spot under an electron microscope, or put it in an incubator and then candle it to view progress.

- Even when the time is up in the incubator or under a broody, eggs may candle blank but this is no proof that they were not fertile at the beginning. They could have been started for 24 hours and stopped, then left to die. They would candle blank but were all originally fertile.

- You should crack open all the non-hatched eggs after you've completed incubation; it may give you a clue as to the reasons why they failed. Stopped half way; fully-formed but dead-in-shell; addled and smelly; adhered to shell... these are all reasons completely out of the supplier's control.

sale items every week, but who is to say that they are actually what's being claimed? Ideally you should do some careful checking into the reputation of the seller by reading the feedback rating; too many negatives should undoubtedly warn you to steer well clear.

Be prepared

Try to think logically about your new venture. All too often people fail to appreciate the obvious pitfalls. They rush into the whole process with inadequate research and preparation, and often purchase mixed breeds and colours which fragments success into too many options.

If you buy a dozen hatching eggs and start the incubation process,

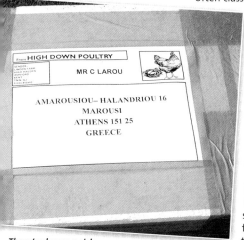

There's always a risk attached when entrusting hatching eggs to the delivery services.

don't imagine that all 12 are going to produce cute, fluffy chicks. An excellent result would be nine eggs hatching, but more normally you're likely to end up with six chicks. Unfortunately, it's not unheard of for results to be much worse, with maybe just three or four eggs hatching or – in the worst case – none at all. There are no guarantees as far as fertility is concerned.

But assuming that some of the eggs do produce chicks, then you must be prepared for about half of the birds to be males, which raises the question of what are you going to do with those? Unless you're hatching top-quality pure breeds, it's almost impossible to find genuine homes for unwanted cockerels. And since cockrels are often classed as a nuisance by local councils, you'll need to be prepared to cull them if you can't find homes for them and can't keep them yourself. My advice is that you purchase a maximum of 12 eggs of one breed and colour; you thereby stand a better chance of a few hens for your back garden.

Postman Pat

Having located your source of hopefully fertile eggs, it's unlikely that the vendor is going to be on your doorstep, so that throws up the immediate problem

of delivery. Ideally, personal collection is the best option but in most cases this simply isn't a practical option.

Getting them delivered means entrusting them either to the postal service or a parcel delivery operator, neither of which will necessarily be particularly gentle with the cargo. With this in mind, good packing is essential to help maximise the chance of the eggs arriving safely and in one piece. You can buy special polystyrene modules to hold the eggs securely inside the parcel but, despite these, some carriers still manage to shake the life out of them... and of course the breeder then gets the blame for supplying duff eggs!

My advice is to check all the eggs on arrival. Before setting them under a broody hen or in your incubator, use a candling light to inspect the condition of the air sac, which you'll find at the blunt end of the shell. This should be clearly visible and intact. If it's not, or appears to be full of bubbles, then it's pointless incubating the egg

HATCHING EGG RULES

Many a Fancier swears by broody hens, especially those with Silkies, but give *me* a good, old-fashioned incubator any time. Anyway, whatever your hatching preference, here are my top egg-related tips to bear in mind.

- When your eggs arrive, candle them to check the condition of the air sac (look for rupturing), then inspect the shell for signs of dents or cracks. If you're unhappy then call the supplier without delay; don't wait until 21 days later!

- After arrival, allow the eggs to settle for 24 hours before setting them in an incubator or under a broody hen.

- Any soiling on the shells should be removed with a dry scouring pad. Do not wash them – this is particularly important with waterfowl eggs as many have a natural protective, waxy coating which shouldn't be removed.

- Follow the instructions from the incubator manufacturer, paying particular attention to temperature and humidity.

- Never site the incubator in direct sunlight or in a centrally-heated room. Equally, don't put it in a chilly shed, or garage, where the ambient temperature is too low.

- Don't keep opening the incubator to check on progress; you'll simply destroy the environment created. Remember, the temperature in small incubators can drop rapidly following lid opening, with disasterous results.

- Try not to set mixed batches as their incubation time requirements will be different.

- There are different hatching times for poultry and waterfowl; always adhere to the incubator manufacturer's recommendations.

- It's worth candling the eggs after 10-12 days to check on fertility. Any egg that's evidently 'clear' should be discarded; if left it can cause others to be contaminated and spoil.

- Three days before hatching is due, stop turning the eggs and increase the humidity. Don't spray the eggs with water as this can chill them.

- Let the chicks emerge from their shells naturally. Any having difficulty shouldn't be helped by picking away the shell. Let nature take its course, hard though this may be to do.

- The chicks are quite safe to remain in the incubator resting from the ordeal of hatching; they don't need water or food for 24 hours, and must be given time to dry thoroughly.

- After 24 hours move the chicks into a brooder with a heat lamp, and give them fresh, clean water and a good quality chick crumb.

- All un-hatched eggs should be discarded.

because this sort of rupturing of the air sac due to rough handling means that it'll never hatch.

Bless 'em all!

While much focus is placed on rogue traders, this doesn't quite represent the full picture with regard to problematic egg sales. Although most customers are genuine and are only seeking successful hatchings, there is a proportion of people always looking to exploit the system. One common trick is to aim to bag a dozen free eggs simply by complaining that all the ones sent were duds, regardless of whether they actually were or not. It never fails to surprise me how many people actually try this!

I hatch all my breeds throughout the season from January to July, and am fully aware if any of my cockerels have fertility issues. I see problems long before they can ever reach the customer. So, while I'm getting a hatch rate of 65-75% from my Copper Black Marans, it's interesting to get a call from a customer saying all the eggs I sent were infertile. Strangely, they never remember to mention that the broody didn't sit tight and kept leaving the eggs to get cold, or the incubator was in the airing cupboard...

It is worth remembering that traditionally the hatching season runs from early spring through to mid-summer (February to July). The large breeds are best hatched as early as possible, so that they can make the best of the good weather and grow big and strong before winter arrives. Bantams are best hatched late, as these birds need to be small and to fall within the weight limits set in their particular breed standard.

The time between setting the egg (beginning incubation) and point-of-lay (maturity) is typically 22 weeks; nearly six months. So its obvious, with this in mind, that hatching eggs in August gives insufficient daylight and warmth for the birds to grow and mature. Consequently, birds hatched this late are likely to be sickly and small, and will tend never to catch up – it's simply not worth your effort.

Fertility is a function of the cock birds being interested in mating. In January, February and March 2008, our weather went from days of pouring rain to freezing cold and back again. So it's not surprising there can be patchy fertility in the spring, and anyone purchasing eggs during this period should be prepared for some infertile ones in every dozen.

Success of failure?

Providing you have chosen your supplier well you should, by and large, be successful. However, if your hatch proves a disaster, don't automatically blame the egg supplier. Check all the variable factors under your control, particularly the incubator temperature reading using a different thermometer and the relative humidity. Also, don't dismiss the possibility of others fiddling with the incubator while your back is turned; children can find them almost irresistible!

I supply eggs to many customers and nothing pleases me more than when I get a call to tell me how delighted they were with their results; it's infinitely better than having complaints, so why would any supplier contrive to cheat customers?

Dudley Mallett runs High Down Poultry, based near Ashford, Kent. He produces pure breed stock as well as hybrid layers, and you can find out more by calling 01233 850692, sending an email to: dudley.mallett@btinternet.com or visiting the website at: www.highdownpoultry.co.uk

Checking progress

Terry Beebe provides some hints and tips on candling – the simple but effective way of observing exactly what's going on inside a hatching egg

During the course of the incubation process there's a definite need to check the development of the eggs you have set for hatching – it's vital to be sure that what's inside the egg is still alive, and developing correctly. The same applies for eggs being hatched by a broody hen. There's no point in allowing the incubator to run, or let a broody hen sit, with eggs which aren't fertile. Not only is this a waste of time, effort and expense, but it might cause problems too – infertile eggs can pose a disease risk to the fertile ones nearby.

The traditional method used for checking hatching egg fertility is a technique know as candling. It's a simple process involving nothing more than shining a light through the egg from behind, to highlight what's inside. As you might imagine from the name, the process was originally undertaken using a candle but, nowadays, electric lights and torches offer safer and more effective alternatives.

What's inside?

Another big advantage of candling, apart from enabling you to be sure about the important fertility/infertility issue, is that it allows you to monitor the growth process inside the egg. You need to do this for more than just your own interest; charting the correct development is important as it'll enable you to weed-out eggs which aren't right, thus minimising the disease risk.

In days of old, one of the favourite methods for testing the fertility of an egg was to place it in a bucket of warm water. This simple test involved nothing more than noting what the egg did in the water; if it floated or bobbed up and down, then this was a sign that it was fertile. Those which sank to the bottom were pronounced infertile. However, just how reliable this test was remains open to debate, although I'm pretty sure that, as with so many of these traditional methods, there's probably more than a grain of truth to it.

One other approach which is often suggested involves regularly checking the eggs for weight gain

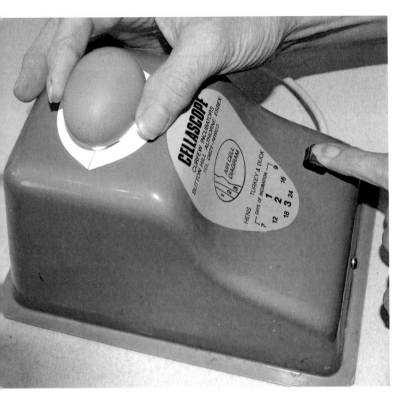

You'll have to pay about £50 for a free-standing candler like this one. Although it does exactly the same job as the torch-type, you do have the luxury of 'hands-free' operation.

or loss, but candling is the quicker, easier and more reliable method.

There's a good range of candling machines on the market these days but, by and large, the most popular seem to be the hand-held models. Their simple design keeps the cost down, and makes them straightforward and effective to use. Flick on the switch, place an egg over the end and in most cases the carefully shielded light will be powerful enough to shine right though and illuminate the whole egg. Where it can get a bit more tricky is when you're working with very dark-shelled eggs, which are obviously much harder to illuminate – the extra shell pigment provides much more of an obstacle. In some instances a high-intensity bulb will be required, in which case care will be needed with its use. These bulbs inevitably generate more heat, so it's not a good idea to keep them focussed on the egg for too long – the embryo inside can be damaged if you don't take care. In reality, each assessment should only take a second or two in front of the light to complete.

Safe hands

There are a number of bench-mounted candlers available as well and, although these are usually more powerful than the hand-held types, they operate in exactly the same way. However, many users consider them more convenient to use, as their design means that you have both hands free to carefully position the egg (and help avoid dropping it!). Irrespective of which type you use, though, it's common sense to do the checking in a darkened room; it just makes everything so much easier, and the all-important contents of the egg so much more visible.

For the more experienced breeder, candling can take place round about day seven of the incubation process but, I do advise that it's better for beginners to wait until day 10. This ensures that everything is just that little bit more developed, and thus visible. As your experience grows, however, you'll learn to tell what development is taking place at a really early age. This ability certainly takes time and patience to develop, but everyone gets better at spotting the signs with practice.

Of course, you'll need to candle your eggs more than once, and I tend to do my chicken eggs for the second time after about 14 days. If

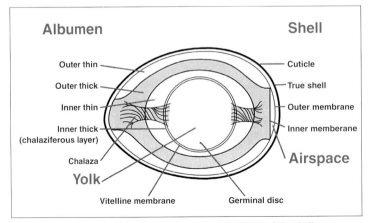

Albumen

Outer thin
Outer thick
Inner thin
Inner thick
(chalaziferous layer)
Chalaza

Yolk

Vitelline membrane   Germinal disc

Shell

Cuticle
True shell
Outer membrane
Inner memberane

Airspace

The structure of an egg. Note the airspace at the 'blunt' end of the shell.

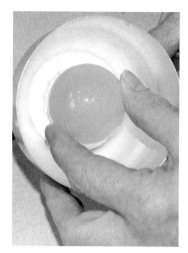

All candlers are built around a simple bulb; it's not exactly rocket science!

you're incubating duck or geese eggs, though, remember that the hatching period is longer; I tend to wait until the 21-day mark.

So what are you actually looking for? Well, the first sign of life is what I call the 'spider', simply because of the way it looks. With a good light shining through you'll clearly be able to see what appears to be a few spider's legs (blood vessels) creeping along the inside of the shell, and a darker, central spot from which they are emanating. From this point onwards, development continues at a steady rate. If there's no sign of the spider-type formation after the first week or ten days, then you're pretty safe to assume that the egg was not fertile in the first place.

Unfortunately, though, the embryos can die at any stage during this early development. A classic sign of this is what's known, slightly ghoulishly, as the 'blood ring'. This is impossible to miss, and takes the form of a dark line which traces its circular way around the inside of the shell. It's a bad sign which should leave you in no doubt that the embryo inside has perished. Losses at this stage are frustrating but there's very little you can do about them, apart from chalking them up to experience. From the moment you first set the eggs in the incubator, to the time that they hatch, there's plenty that can go wrong, resulting in what's generally known as 'dead in shell'. You just have to accept that you'll

rarely achieve a 100% hatch rate, or ineed anything like it, especially if you are new to the hobby.

Look again

As time progresses and the embryo develops inside the egg, candling will reveal a progressively darker-looking mass, and you'll also start to notice the air sac, which forms in the blunt end of the egg. This provides the air the chick needs to breath immediately prior to hatching. Its relative size can be used as a good indicator as to how the hatch is progressing (*see diagram below*).

Once the chick is fully developed, and just about ready to hatch, it then has the job of breaching both the inner and outer shell layer – a process that's known as 'pipping'. This normally takes place about two days before the actual hatching. The chick then works its way progressively around the shell, until a section breaks away and it can get out.

This 'pipping' stage is a very important time; the chick is vulnerable and a lot of losses tend to occur at this stage. While most will 'pip' on time, actually getting out successfully tends to prove a good deal more of a challenge. Variable factors such as humidity and temperature can play their parts, as can the strength of the chick itself. Inferior breeding stock

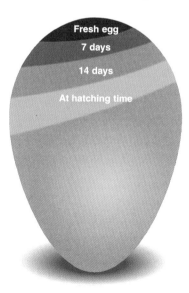

This diagram illustrates how the air space enlarges as the chick develops.

Fresh egg
7 days
14 days
At hatching time

You can buy a simple, hand-held, torch-style candler like this one for about £12.

can be one of the primary causes of a failure to hatch. It's a very sad end for all concerned.

As a general rule, I think that it's best to leave all the eggs inside the incubator/hatcher until those chicks that are going to get out have done so. The time involved here can vary slightly but, to be honest, anything which hasn't managed to hatch successfully after 36 hours is best disposed of. While some breeders are happy to spend time assisting the strugglers out of their shells, in my experience the results are very rarely successful. Often those which are late will be weak or deformed in some way, so their prospects will be poor. I apologise if this approach upsets some people, but I can only tell it as it is. There are exceptions, but they are few and far between.

The most important lesson to learn about any part of incubation is the gathering of knowledge. You can read as much as you like and ask questions (both recommended), but there really is no substitute for personal experience. Only by trying things yourself will your confidence grow and your results improve. •

Problem chicks

Don't imagine that breeding chickens is all sweetness and light –
Terry Beebe explains why it often isn't

When everyone gears-up for a new breeding season, I always fully expect the usual crop of questions and queries from enthusiastic keepers experiencing problems with their hatching. It's the same every year, as people get both frustrated and annoyed as things go wrong; it can be a very disappointing business.

But it's important to appreciate that both incubation and hatching are enmeshed in a complicated web of variable and inter-related factors, all of which have the potential to upset the balance and hinder successful hatching. Everyone, even experienced breeders, should expect incubation problems every now and then.

Unfortunately, it's inevitably those newest to the hobby who tend to suffer the most, particularly if they are using low-spec incubators from the cheaper end of the scale.

Problems, problems

Of course, experiencing problems is one thing, but sorting out the reason for them can be quite another. It's a regrettable fact that lots can go wrong; chicks can hatch with serious defects, they can fail to get out of the shell – dying in the process – or they can die at some point earlier in the incubation term. The best ways to counter the likelihood of these sorts of problem occurring are to be completely confident about the correct

operation of your incubator, and to use only the best, fresh and fertile hatching eggs.

Human nature being what it is, though, many newcomers to hatching tend to rush into the incubation process without bothering to fully understand exactly what's involved. Apart from egg quality, the two major stumbling blocks for a lot of people seem to be incubator temperature and humidity; get either of these wrong and hatch rates will be poor. Egg turning is another important factor which those using basic machines, without automatic turning mechanisms, often neglect.

Understanding the cause of hatching troubles is the vital

requirement, because it allows you to improve your technique to avoid similar problems in the future. So, to help with this, I'm going to run through some of the most common hatching problems encountered, explaining the most likely causes in each case.

Breeding stock

If you decide to produce your own hatching eggs, then you must take time to maximise your chances of success by carefully selecting your breed stock. Only choose birds which are obviously fit and healthy, and always breed from stock of a standard that you wish to reproduce. Avoid obvious defects like bent toes, twisted beaks, poor combs etc, as most of these undesirable faults will be carried forward into the offspring. Poor quality breeders will always result in poor quality youngsters.

It also makes sense to ensure that the breeding birds are well through the moult, have no parasite infestations and that they are the correct weight. Birds which are either too thin or too fat won't breed well. The age factor is important too; pick breeding stock that's in the prime of life. The best breeding stock will be in good condition too, enjoying plenty of fresh air, exercise and a good quality diet with vitamin supplement. The latter is very important in my view; vitamin deficiencies can be a significant factor in poor hatchability.

As a general rule, expert breeders will expect to hatch, on average, about 85% of the eggs they set in the incubator. However, this sort of success rate is a little unrealistic for the hobby keeper whose efforts are limited by inexperience and generally inferior incubation equipment. So, for most beginners, it's reasonable to expect to hatch about 65% of the eggs being incubated.

However, the hatching odds can be more stacked against you if you decide to work with one of the breeds carrying what's termed a 'lethal gene'. Breeds affected in this way usually present very low hatching rates; the Japanese is probably one of the best-known breeds affected in this way. Others which can suffer in a similar sort of

Dead-in-the-shell is always an upsetting incubation outcome, particularly if you have young children expecting fluffy chicks.

way include the Sebright and Hamburgh – weak embryos caused by very close breeding. So my advice to beginners is to play safe, make things as easy as possible and to opt for breeds that don't bring with them this sort of 'hatching baggage'.

Hatching failures

The first and most obvious cause of a hatching failure is an infertile egg (these should be weeded out of the incubator following candling), often caused by an infertile cockerel. Other possibilities include poor egg storage, serious contamination, eggs that have become chilled and

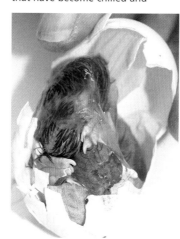

There are plenty of reasons why chicks can die before they hatch; incubation is a balancing act.

power cuts. Infertility among your birds can be promoted by infestations of lice, fleas and the dreaded Red Mite – all of these conditions need immediate attention and treatment. If infertility is a big problem and there's no obvious cause, then simply try another cockerel.

In my experience, the top four hatching problems are as follows:

Stuck in shell

This is the most common of all hatching problems, and the temperature of the incubator is one of the main causes; normally it's been set too high. The trouble arises because the high temperature dries out the shell and the membrane beneath it, imprisoning the chick. The shell becomes too hard, and the membrane turns into a tough, rubbery barrier. The unfortunate consequence is that, try as it might, the chick is unable to break out, so it dies.

A lack of humidity can also be a major cause of this problem, promoting drying and toughening

PREMATURE DEATH

Egg death at:	Possible causes:
1-2 days	The eggs are too old and have been stored for too long before being incubated. Also, incubator temperature fluctuating, or set incorrectly. Inbreeding can be another cause.
1-7 days	Incubator temperature too high or too low, or fluctuating. Poor ventilation inside the unit. Poor turning – eggs must be turned regularly. Hot or cold spots inside the incubator – more common in still-air units.
12-18 days	Temperature incorrect – ensure the thermometer is set at the right height in the incubator, just above the eggs. Humidity incorrect, poor turning, bacteria build-up and/or poor hygiene. Eggs too old, temperature surge or loss.

Maximise your hatching potential by picking a breed that's known to be 'incubator-friendly', such as Light Sussex or Welsummer.

of the shell and membrane. To avoid trouble, humidity needs to be set at about 60-70% for the last few days before hatching.

'Sticky' chicks

Chicks which appear to struggle to hatch, and seem abnormally 'sticky', can be suffering from high humidity levels and/or low temperatures. These conditions tend to promote excess moisture inside the shell which, in extreme cases, can cause the chicks to drown.

One of the best ways to control this is to ensure the vents in the incubator are open, allowing the flow of air to increase as hatching day approaches. This will reduce humidity and so lower fluid levels inside the egg. Be aware, though, that there's a very fine line between a chick being too wet and too dry inside its shell.

Splayed legs

This unfortunate condition, which prevents the chicks from walking, is normally the result of the incubator temperature being too high. But it

can also be a genetic condition passed on from the parents, or caused by the young chicks slipping and 'doing the splits' on the smooth incubator/brooder floor. To avoid the latter, always make sure the youngsters have a suitable 'grippy' surface (cardboard can work well) on which to walk.

Crooked toes

This condition, and a general weakness in the young birds, can be promoted by incorrect incubator temperatures (too high or low) combined with poor ventilation. Poor diet in the breeding stock can be another important contributory factor not to be overlooked.

A classic case of twisted-toe.

Assistance needed?

One of the hatching-related questions I'm most often asked relates to whether or not chicks which appear to be struggling should be helped out of their shells. This is always a tricky dilemma, and much depends on the sort of breeder you are, and the amount of time you've got to spend on assisting 'strugglers'.

If you do decide to have a go, then take things slowly and be very gentle. Only ever break tiny pieces of shell away at a time (using tweezers), and take care not to cause the chick to start bleeding. You'll need to be patient and delicate, and there really are no guarantees that the chick will survive.

The more matter-of-fact breeders argue that the chick has failed to hatch for a reason, and so it's 'just not meant to be'. This point of view suggests that, even if the chick does live on, it'll experience problems with development and more than likely grow into a weak, sub-standard adult.

Personally, I always tend to try and help the hatch if it looks at all hopeful, but I'm fully aware that the prospects for outright success are limited.

Disease hotbed?

Remember, also, that your innocent-looking incubator can be an absolute hotbed of disease and infection if you're not careful. As well as providing the ideal environment for the development of hatching eggs, the warm, damp interiors of these machines can also offer the perfect breeding ground for bacteria.

Eggs with dirty or damaged shells, or incubators that are allowed to get dirty, can lead to serious hatching problems. The shells, being permeable, offer little resistance against aggressive bacteria, and the delicate embryos within are certainly vulnerable to this sort of attack.

Egg shells and incubators must be carefully and effectively cleaned before each hatching process begins, using specialist products that will clear these bacterial risks. Your local poultry product supplier should be able to advise about which treatments to use.

Inside story

An 'official' hatching egg, of the best available type and dimensions; stamped to identify.

Hans L Schippers explains the ins and outs of the hatching process – an event which still fascinates him after many years as a poultry breeder

Regardless of how many times I follow the poultry hatching process, I still never fail to be amazed and deeply impressed by the fantastic transformation which takes place in such a relatively short space of time. The development from yolk to baby chick is simply wonderful!

In just 21 days, a completely new chicken is created within its breathable shell and, as part of a recent research program, I thought it would be in teresting to document and photograph the major changes which occur during this momentous three-week period of growth.

Hatching basics
Before I get down to the nitty-gritty, it's perhaps worth taking a moment or two to consider some of

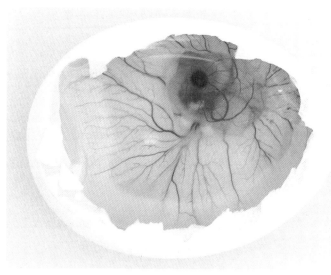

From Day 8 the head starts developing fast. Beak, legs and wings start to develop quickly too.

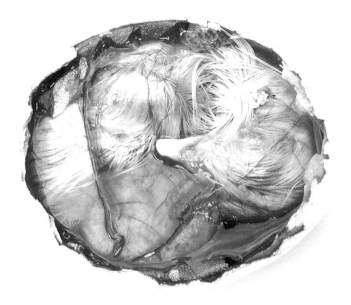

On Day 17, despite appearing well developed and showing fluff feathers, the chick is not ready to hatch. Significant changes will occur over the coming two days. The yolk is still large.

helped by the often inadequate instructions provided with this entry-level equipment.

As with so much else associated with the breeding and keeping of poultry, there's simply no substitute for experience when it comes to hatching eggs effectively; a little knowledge can be a dangerous thing! For example, plenty of people often lay the blame for no sign of embryo development on the fact that an egg is infertile, but fail to appreciate the cause. It could well be that there's a problem with the cockerel that's been 'serving' the hens or, indeed, one of the parents could be infertile. Egg incubation relies for its success on a whole host of variable factors; any one of which, if wrong, could be responsible for a development problem within the egg.

Food reserves

To be a good and effective hatching egg, its contents must contain adequate levels of the high-quality foodstuffs which are essential to nourish and nurture the chick during its rapid development. Shortfalls in this respect will almost certainly lead to the pre-hatch death of the chick; an unfortunate condition commonly and graphically known as 'dead-in-shell'.

the more general aspects associated with the hatching process.

Good hatching results are entirely dependent on starting with good hatching eggs in the first place. Other vital factors such as temperature, humidity and ventilation must all be correct too but, without fertile eggs from healthy hens, hatch rates will be low.

While using a broody hen to hatch eggs is the most natural

approach, many keepers prefer the relative convenience of using an incubator in place of the hen. However, the wide variation in quality and effectiveness of the machines on the market means that success can be a bit of a hit and miss affair for the inexperienced breeder. Without a good understanding of the incubation basics, achieving reliably consistent results using a budget-priced machine can be a real struggle. The prospects aren't

The age of the egg is another very important factor. Its hatchability reduces as it gets older and, with this in mind, it's never really worth trying to hatch any egg that is more than ten days old. In addition, the way in which the egg has been stored prior to incubation is a significant issue too; temperature extremes should be avoided and it should be turned frequently to prevent the yolk from settling into one position.

This potential for eggs to be stored for a little while before the incubation process actually begins allows us the opportunity to transport them over long distances – even from continent to continent. This has proved to be a significant factor in helping to promote interest in some of our rarest breeds, which is all to the good. Inevitably, there is a downside, and it is that, as a general rule, the further an egg travels the more the chances of a successful hatch are reduced. In my experience, this

By Day 19 the chick will have turned itself so its head is nearer the air sac. The yolk is now tiny, having been mostly absorbed into the belly.

does seem to vary from one breed to another, and the good news is that I've certainly found that some do travel very well!

Finally, don't forget that transported eggs need to be rested for at least 24 hours after arrival, before the incubation process begins, so this time needs to be built into your calculations regarding the overall timescale.

The chart included with this article provides a summary of exactly what's happening inside the egg during the incubation period. It's a period of intense activity as you'll see and, all being well, the process concludes with the moment of truth when the chick finally breaks free to begin its life in the big world!

The effort involved in physically chipping away enough of the shell to allow hatching is considerable for the chick, and so most will pause for a while before trying to stand, starting to walk and allowing themselves to dry out. It's at this point that owners need to carry out a general inspection to establish that all's well. Chicks should be examined to make sure that all the vitals are present and correct – eyes, beak, legs, vent and navel. Oddities found at this stage are a problem, as you'll then be faced with the decision about what to do with them. Much, of course, depends on why you're breeding in the first place; for exhibition purposes or simply to increase the number of birds in your flock.

Sub-standard birds are of little use to the experienced exhibitor, and so will be weeded-out at an early stage. This may sound a little harsh but birds with deformities and other problems will not make good future breeders, and may also pose a health risk to the others around them. However, domestic keepers might be more inclined to keep and nurse a poorly chick. There are important welfare issues to consider too, and it's vital for all keepers to avoid allowing any of their birds to suffer.

In conclusion, it's no exaggeration to say that good hatching is like good rearing; it's an art! Learning from your experiences is the key aspect, although a theoretical knowledge of what's going on helps as well. •

WHAT'S GOING ON?

Day 1 Cell development begins at the 'blastoderm'; a layer of cells found on the upper side of the yolk.

Day 2 The construction of heart and blood vessels starts, together with the development of some muscle blocks (somites). The eyes and ears are already differentiated at this early stage.

Day 3 Development continues with the first appearance of the vertebral column, the addition of more blood vessel extension and the formation of limb buds.

Day 4 The heart starts to beat visibly. Three parts of the brain are visible too.

Day 5 The embryo starts to look like a chicken, and some major organs become visible for the first time.

Day 6 The blood vessels of the yolk membrane grow and become visible when the egg is 'candled' (contents viewed using a bright backlight). Doing this will reveal a pair of dark spots – one on either side of the heart – which are the eyes. Development of the tongue and larger organs begins.

Day 7 Legs and wings are now in development, and digits become visible.

Day 8 The upper and lower mandibles (the bird's beak) start to grow. Legs and wings begin development too. The skull encases the brain and the neck grows longer. Feather roots begin developing on the skin.

Day 9 The eyes are now easily visible, as are the digits on the feet; separation of the digits of the feet begins.

Day 10 The size of the air sac is visibly increased, and the scales on the chick's legs begin to show.

Day 11 By this stage the developing bird is very obviously a chick. You'll also be able to see the tiny 'egg tooth' (used to chip through the shell at hatching time) developing on the upper mandible. Intestines should show clearly too.

Day 12 The down begins to grow now from the feather follicles on the skin.

Day 13 The skeleton starts to calcify.

Day 14 The embryo rotates so that the chick's head is at the wide end of the egg, close to the air sac.

Day 15 Down and toenails are present now and continue to grow quickly.

Day 16 Most of the remaining albumen (the 'white' of the egg) has been absorbed now; the scales on the legs and the toenails harden.

Day 17 The amniotic fluid will lessen and the chick now occupies all the available space inside the shell. The neck and breast muscles grow rapidly, and are very important because their strength is needed for successful hatching.

Day 18 The remainder of the yolk begins to retract into the chick's belly, ready to act as a source of food during the first few days after hatching. Egg turning (in an incubator) should stop at this point, and the humidity should be raised to 65-70%.

Day 19 Chick's position inside the shell is fixed with its head at the air sac end and its feet at the pointed end of the shell.

Day 20 With help of leg, neck, breast and wing muscles, the chick forces its egg tooth through the membrane into the air sac and, from there, out through the shell. Increased humidity levels inside an incubator help with this vital stage. Eggs being naturally brooded by a hen can be sprinkled with a little, luke-warm water at this time for the same reason. It's the pressure of the chick against the internal shell membrane which stops the blood vessels from bleeding. Up until this point, the chick has been sourcing its oxygen through the porous shell, hence the need for blood flow here. But, when conventional respiration begins, this creates an increase in carbon dioxide levels which, in turn, provides the stimulus for the chick to start piercing the shell (known as pipping).

Day 21 As hatching continues the chick will turn itself inside the shell, in an anti-clockwise direction, chipping away small pieces of shell with its egg tooth as it does so. It can take anything from 12 to 20 hours for the chick to break its way out, and it will rest frequently during this exhausting task. Hatching times vary from breed to breed.

Incubation adventures

My three Sebastopol goslings, successfully hatched in the R-Com 20 incubator.

Gail Harland offers a personal account of the highs and lows she experienced in her first season with an incubator

Relying on broody hens to hatch eggs can sometimes be a bit of a gamble. Even the most dedicated sitter may abandon a clutch if she gets upset, and heavy birds – like my much-loved but clumsy Cochin hen – can accidentally break eggs.

So when I sold off a lot of spare snowdrops on eBay – serious snowdrop collectors will pay inflated prices for a single bulb of special varieties – I decided to use

the money to buy myself an electronic incubator.

Automatic option

I settled on a R-COM 20, which sounded easy to use, with automatic temperature and humidity controls and egg-turning. I read the manual and was informed that these machines are calibrated in the factory, so all that was required was to set the

required temperature and humidity. I went for the suggested options of 37.5°C and 45% humidity, then added 12 gold Silkie and six Araucana eggs and began the difficult business of waiting patiently for three weeks.

After 23 days I was faced with the sad conclusion that none of the eggs were going to hatch and, as it seemed unlikely that they were all infertile, I started to think about

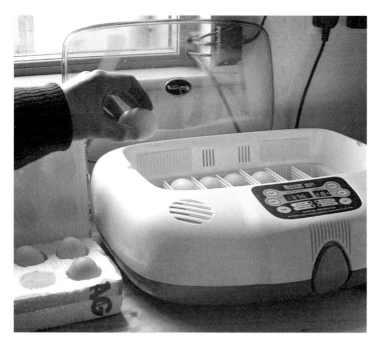

maintain humidity, decided to improvise with wet flannels in the incubator instead.

Having read conflicting reports about the importance of humidity with waterfowl eggs during incubation, I didn't want to take chances. But, after a few nights of getting up at 3am to top-up the water, I inevitably overslept and came down to find the humidity registered at 'lo' according to the machine's display read-out, indicating less than 20%.

Not so bad

As it turned out, though, the humidity problem didn't turn out to be a serious one; four of the six goose eggs were fertile and continued to develop, although I lost one on hatching. However, if anyone reading this is considering buying one of these incubators, my advice would be to make sure that you get a 2008; the machine has been updated and no longer requires the sponge as a humidity control device. Sadly, my supplier declined to replace my machine for the newer version!

I also set six Cayuga duck eggs and ten Black East Indian ones (I'd asked for six but was supplied ten, which was very kind but did cause problems trying to squeeze them all into the incubator!). Five of each type were fertile and hatched successfully. Having invested in a candling torch, I was able to check progress and remove the infertile eggs, thus making more space for the others.

After hatching, I kept the goslings and ducks in the incubator for 24 hours, then transferred them to my plant propagator, which makes a useful little brooder as it has a thermostatically-controlled base and a large plastic dome-style top. After a few days, they were spending the day in a box in the kitchen or a run outside (depending on the weather), then returning to the propagator at night. It's amazing how quickly they grow, and it wasn't long before they required a very large box in our lean-to.

Meanwhile, it seemed a shame to leave the incubator idle, so I acquired an assorted batch of chicken eggs to hatch.

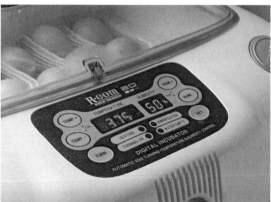

I had humidity and temperature troubles with my R-Com, but the machine has given me some great birds too.

what might have gone wrong. Putting our household thermometer into the incubator quickly revealed the explanation; the temperature inside was just 29°C.

With a sigh I disposed of the eggs and took the incubator apart to clean it out, only then to discover a further problem. The sponge that's used inside to control the humidity had disintegrated. Apparently, these are meant to last for about a year, and should be boiled after each use to ensure effective sterilisation.

So I contacted the supplier and was told that my experience wasn't unknown, and that I'd be sent a replacement sponge. After two new ones were lost in the post,

they finally sent another by registered post, and it arrived safely. However, in the meantime, I'd taken the opportunity of setting some Sebastopol goose eggs and, with no sponge to

My blue Cochin proved to be an excellent surrogate mother. She turned broody at just the right time.

Here are some day-old, white-crested black Poland chicks – another success story!

Of these, six Penedesencas plus three each of the other breeds hatched. Fortunately, from a rearing point of view, my Cochin hen had gone broody at the same time, and had hatched two of my Sultan eggs. So, as the chicks hatched in the incubator, I took them outside and put them under the hen. This worked really well, I'm delighted to report, and she and her mate continued being perfect parents to all 14 youngsters.

Another batch

The next batch of chicks to hatch (some white-crested black Polands from Terry Beebe's eggs, and blue Silkies from Cherry Barlow) I had had to look after myself. This, though, was a pleasure rather than a chore, and has ensured that these chicks are much tamer than they might otherwise have been. The Polands, in particular, are really affectionate and love to sit on your shoulder and pretend to be parrots! Indeed, they can make walking around the garden quite difficult as they are always getting underfoot.

I had heard about Penedesencas, a breed from the Catalan region of Spain, that lay very dark, brown-shelled eggs, like those from the Marans. I visited a breeder in Essex and came away with seven eggs from her black Penedesencas. I also got some Marans, some Araucanas and, from eBay again, six Appenzeller eggs.

This is one of my five, very cute, newly-hatched Cayuga ducklings.

The most difficult thing I've found with artificial incubation is knowing whether or not to intervene if a chick seems to be having problems hatching. I know that opinions vary greatly on this subject, with one school of thought suggesting that if they can't get out of the shell themselves, then something's the matter and they should be left. The alternative view of course is that it's always worth trying to help.

I helped two of the goslings who seemed to be making no progress 24 hours after initial chipping. One of them subsequently died so I worry that I perhaps interfered too soon, but the other is now a thriving goose. Of the chicks, I helped two Marans to hatch. Marans seemed to have particularly tough eggshells, and certainly needed the extra assistance. An Araucana that had chipped but not progressed died in its shell on a day when I was not around to help, so I don't know if I would have been able to save it.

After a busy season in the artificial incubator, I still think that every bird that hatches is a miracle, and any one I lose I regard as nothing less than a tragedy. •

One-week-old ducklings and goslings sharing a run and enjoying the sunshine together.

Cheep goods

Steve Holmes discovers that it's perfectly possible to hatch quail from shop-bought eggs

The incubator was standing empty and we were wondering what to hatch next. We'd been successful with eggs from our bantams and some Wyandotte hatching eggs before, but had decided to try something a bit different this time.

I'd heard that it is possible to hatch quail from eggs bought from a supermarket, so thought we'd give that a try ourselves. We eventually tracked down what looked to be suitable eggs at our local supermarket, and I bought a couple of dozen. They cost less that £5 so, even if the whole project failed completely, we didn't stand to lose too much!

Teething troubles

The Octagon 20 was set up and, after accidentally cracking one of the tiny eggs, the remaining 23 were set. Things didn't go terribly smoothly in the early stages; we had problems maintaining the correct level of humidity inside the incubator. Then the electricity supply company decided to turn the power off on the seventh day for maintenance work, and so we were forced to move the incubator to a relative's house in the next village.

What's more, our overall planning wasn't too good either, because on the day that we were expecting the young quails to hatch (day 19), we were booked-up for a weekend away!

Our first two quail chicks, one-day old.

My job involves night work and, on the evening of day 17, my wife Margot gave me a call to let me know that she'd heard cheeping coming from the incubator, and that a couple of the eggs had pipped. At that stage we hadn't got round to taking the incubator off the cradle, so Margot moved it on to the lounge table so that she could keep a better eye on progress. She also added more water to bring the humidity up. Then, at just after 11pm that evening, our first chick hatched, and the second one followed at 6am. As it turned out, this was to be the last, as none of the other eggs hatched. But just to get two tiny chicks from a supermarket-bought batch of eggs was a real surprise!

New home

By this stage we were pretty well prepared, and had made a brooder out of an electric propagator, with a layer of sand covered in brown paper to stop the chicks eating it. The young birds were moved in that evening. We also gave them the cardboard tube from a kitchen roll to provide a bit of shelter, and ground-down some chick crumb to make it as palatable for them as possible.

As I write this, the young pair are doing well and have reached the ripe old age of ten days! We're still not too sure about their breed, but I think they are probably Coturnix. They have developed into healthy, active chicks, and even attempted to fly the other day... and, they love singing to us! Flushed with success, we have just set another couple of dozen eggs and, assuming things go more smoothly this time, it'll be interesting to see if the hatch rate improves.

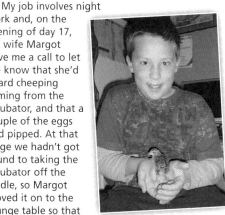
My son Jack – then aged ten – with one of the pair of quails at the ten-day mark.

From incubator to brooder

Brooding is the final stage of the incubation process, but it's also the one which has the potential to become the most frustrating of all. Terry Beebe explains how to get it right

Brooding is an important stage of a chick's life. All the conditions must be right to ensure healthy development and growth.

Hatching the chicks with an incubator is all well and good but, unfortunately, what can tend to happen (especially if you're a beginner) is that a disappointingly high number of chicks will be lost during the vital, early stages of the brooding period.

There are several reasons that can account for these losses, and our aim here is to guide beginners through the potential pitfalls, and thus help maximise survival rates. But the story doesn't end there, because chicks remain vulnerable immediately after the brooding stage has finished, and the heat has been turned off. So we'll also look

at how best to get young birds through this crucial transitional stage too, so they can grow-on into good, healthy stock.

Incubator to brooder

When the hatch is complete, and the chicks are fully dry and fluffy, they're ready to be transferred to the brooder. Obviously, moving very young birds out of an enclosed incubator is a potentially stressful and dangerous operation. Temperature is a key issue, and it's very important that the youngsters aren't plunged into a dramatically cooler environment. So you must take care to ensure that your incubator and brooder temperatures are as similar as you can make them. At this stage the incubator should be set at 37.8°C,

so this is the figure you should work to with the brooder, whether you're using a heat lamp or an 'electric hen'.

Personally I prefer to carry out the transfer during the afternoon, since this gives me time during the evening to make several checks on them with regard to their comfort and temperature, and it allows them that night to rest before being fed in the morning. Another thing I always do is move the chicks in a warm, lined box, to avoid them becoming chilled. This is particularly important if your brooder is in another room or shed. Once chicks of this age get chilled, losses are inevitable.

Over the first two weeks or so, it's important to keep the chicks at a pretty constant temperature.

Remember that they are extremely vulnerable at this stage, and very sensitive to temperature extremes at both ends of the scale; too hot can be just as deadly as too cold. After the first couple of weeks, when the chicks' first feathers start growing, you can begin reducing the temperature gradually, by about 2°C a week. This process of gradual reduction should be continued until about the 6-7-week mark, when the heat can usually be switched off as the birds will be adequately feathered.

However, the crucial point to understand is that this temperature progression really is a guide and in every case you should be guided by the day-to-day behaviour of the chicks. Ambient temperatures can obviously play a big part in things too. Thankfully, you can tell a great deal about how suitable the brooder temperature is simply by looking at what the chicks are doing.

If you find the birds tightly bunched under the lamp, then this is a sign that they are too cold. The associated danger with this behaviour is that the act of huddling can cause losses due to suffocation. Alternatively, chicks which are spread out around the edges of the brooder, away from the heat source, indicates that the temperature is too great. When things are just right, the birds should be moving happily around

the enclosure, sometimes under the heat source and, other times, away from it.

Brooder types

There are essentially only three options when it comes to brooder types; enclosures or boxes fitted with a heat lamp (either infrared or 'dull emitter' lamps), those which use a heater called an 'electric hen' or, most traditionally of all, a broody hen.

In fact, the latter can be the easiest way of brooding your chicks, and a good broody is always a real asset to any breeding program. The chicks will build up their own immunity to disease and, in a lot of cases, they tend to be very fit and healthy.

There are downsides though, as the hen and chicks will have to be segregated well away from any other birds you have, and protected from the risk of rodent attack at night. There's also the potential risk posed by parasite infestation (lice and red mite), which will attack, weaken and even possibly kill both the broody and her chicks. Consequently, regular parasite checks must be made and any infestations dealt with rapidly and effectively.

Of the artificial brooder options, I think that the heat lamp/brooder box combination is probably the most popular. These range from

A plastic 'brooder ring' like this is available from specialist poultry outlets. It's simply clipped together to make a circular brooder enclosure wherever you want. It costs about £25.

custom-built units to nothing more complicated than a cardboard box with a light bulb suspended above it. The fact that you can convert anything from an old drawer to a box into a makeshift brooder means that this is an economical and inexpensive way to brood your chicks. But you should be aware that it's often more difficult to control the temperature effectively in a home-made unit and, also, you must be extra vigilant against the risk of fire (particularly if using a cardboard box).

However, today's heat lamps are very easy and safe to use; most are

This is my simple, home-made brooder unit. It measures 30x14in, and has a capacity of about 25 chicks.

Suspending a heat lamp above the brooder allows its height to be simply varied to adjust the heat inside as required.

Infrared heat lamps come in a range of wattages; this one is a red-light producer.

Three variations on the heat lamp theme.

fitted with a protective mesh which protects you and the birds from the bulb's surface heat. They also come with cable and a chain so that they can be simply suspended (and adjusted for height) above the floor of the brooder.

The heat from these lamps is controlled in various ways. First you have the option of varying bulb wattages (250W, 175W, 100W or 60W). This range gives a wide spread of heat options, but the chain on the lamp is also there to provide simple adjustment – raise the bulb to reduce the heat, and vice versa.

There are three main types of bulbs, depending on personal preference; 'white light', infrared heat and 'dull emitter'. The white and red are both actually infra-heat bulbs, and provide a constant source of heat as well as allowing the young birds to see as they feed and drink. The dull emitter, on the other hand, comes in a similar range of wattage sizes, but the difference with these is that they provide heat without light. The bulbs are ceramic, and are approximately twice the price of the traditional glass variety. They do, however, have a very long life span.

The cost of heat lamps and bulbs tend to vary but a fair price is about £20 for a complete set-up. It's possible to buy units which are fitted with a switch that reduces the output by half – in other words, a 250W bulb can be converted into a 125W at the flick of a switch.

These types are generally a little more expensive, but some breeders find them worth the extra cost.

Another alternative, of course, is to make use of a dimmer switch. Once wired into the light circuit, they will infinitely vary the output – and so the heat – of the lamp, so a 250W can be adjusted to meet all your heating requirements. I've always used them, and find them a reliable, convenient and cost-effective control solution.

The electric hen

This unlikely-sounding device is essentially a heat pad on legs. They come in a variety of sizes, stand on the brooder floor at whatever height is needed, and provide heat for the chicks underneath. The heat is simply adjusted by raising or lowering the pad on its legs. Although electric hens are very easy to use, there are a couple of important aspects to remember.

For a start, the heat from them

Here's an 'electric hen' supported on its adjustable legs. Note that an additional light bulb is required with these heaters.

doesn't spread throughout the brooder as much as it does from a heat lamp, so the chicks have to be underneath the pad to benefit from the warmth. This means that you need to be watchful for any birds which are reluctant to venture underneath – they will quickly perish if not encouraged to do so. Secondly, the fact that there is no light source with an electric hen means that you'll need to rig-up a separate bulb to enable the chicks to see enough to eat and drink properly.

Gas brooders

There are quite a few people who use gas brooders, which are straightforward gas burners that can be suspended or free-standing, and which are connect to a standard Calor gas bottle. Heat adjustment is achieved either via the gas flow valve, or by varying the burner's height, as with a brooder lamp. These units are very effective and easy to adjust, but the big danger with them is that the gas supply runs out without you realising, so this needs to be monitored carefully. They're also fairly expensive, and tend to be an option chosen by those brooding large numbers of chicks.

Keep it clean

Before you even start on a rearing programme, it's vital that all appliances and brooders are thoroughly cleaned. I use Milton for the drinkers and feeders, and Barrier V1 disinfectant for the brooder unit itself. Neither of these products will cause harm to chicks, and both are commonly used by many breeders.

Of course, apart from keeping young birds warm, the other key requirement once they're moved to the brooder is that they start to eat and drink as soon as possible. Often, without the presence of a broody hen to provide a demonstration, they will need to be encouraged to start. I find the best way to do this with the feed is to sprinkle some chick crumb on to a piece of rigid cardboard that's laid on the brooder floor. This allows the chick to see the food easily and, if you then tap the board with your finger, this usually arouses their interest, and encourages them to

Your brooder must be clean and warm before the chicks are transfered to it from the incubator.

peck too, and thus start feeding. As soon as they all start taking an interest in the sprinkled feed, my advice is to start supplying it in a chick tray feeder, which will cut down on wastage.

As far as water is concerned, this must always be supplied (clean and fresh) in a narrow-lipped drinker, so there is no risk of the chicks falling in and drowning. To encourage them to drink, I always dip each one's beak in the water as they are put into the brooder, which normally does the trick.

Coccidiosis

This nasty disease is, I feel, one of the greatest threats to the health of chicks at this early stage in their lives. It's caused by a worm which attacks the gut and can, and will, kill the bird. The outward signs are generally blood in the droppings,

loss of appetite and a droopy, sick-looking demeanour. If you suspect anything like this you should consult your vet immediately, who will be able to confirm the diagnosis, and advise on an appropriate treatment.

The primary contributors to coccidiosis are overcrowding, damp bedding and/or warm, damp weather. The disease is transmitted from bird to bird following contact with contaminated droppings, but it can also be transferred from shed to shed on shoes or boots, and even on equipment like dirty drinkers.

However, if you follow all the basic good husbandry rules – keeping the young birds warm enough, out of drafts, clean, dry, well fed and watered – then you should have few problems and your chicks will grow and develop strongly.

Note the narrow-troughed design of the chick drinker on the right. This is essential to avoid the risk of drownings.

Brooding and rearing

A good brooding environment goes a long way to ensuring that your chicks develop into strong, healthy adults. Terry Beebe highlights some of the factors involved

Having hatched and then been allowed to dry completely in the incubator (this takes about 24 hours), young chicks next need to be transferred to a suitable brooder. As we've already noted, brooder temperature is a vital factor that's worth re-emphasising here.

You must be sure to avoid a significant temperature difference between the incubator and the brooder, so the brooder should be set as close to the 37.5-37.8°C levels used in the incubator as possible. Also, it should be kept at this level for at least the first couple of days

after the move; the temperature can then start to be reduced as the birds begin to grow and develop their feathers.

Pitching the temperature at the right level in relation to the birds' development is another key factor, as getting it wrong can have serious consequences. If you're new to breeding then it's always sensible to talk to – and learn from – those with more experience.

A brooder that's too hot will hinder growth, overall health and can actually promote disease. Dehydration is a common and

serious result, which limits appetite and, therefore, development. Chicks will move themselves as far from the heat source as possible if it's too hot which, ironically, can cause them to become dangerously chilled under certain circumstances.

Low temperatures in the brooder can be just as serious – in fact, possibly more so. Chicks are very intolerant of cold and will certainly die quickly if there is insufficient heat during these important early stages of development. In addition, a chilly environment will cause the birds to huddle together tightly in an attempt to keep warm, and the likelihood is that those in the middle of the group will be suffocated in the crush. Losses of this sort can be unfortunately high.

Brooder types

There are plenty of options in this respect, from the very basic to the high-spec and complex. The choice inevitably comes down to something of a compromise in most cases, being determined essentially by the number of birds involved and the budget available.

At the bottom of the sophistication scale is a simple cardboard box. This can be perfectly adequate for a limited number of birds, assuming it's sturdy, secure and doesn't present a fire risk. Alternatively, you can make good use of an old wooden drawer, although the usual shallowness will mean that a mesh cover will be necessary to prevent the chicks from escaping.

A slightly different approach is to use a 6ft x3ft sheet of strong plastic, which you bend round and fasten to create a circular enclosure. This is easy to use and simple to

To avoid chicks getting pushed into corners by the other birds, they can be simply rounded-off using card or hardboard inserts like this.

keep clean. Also, another big advantage is that there are no corners to worry about. Brooder units with conventional, 'square' corners can pose a threat to young birds; individuals can get squashed into a corner and even suffocated by other birds, especially if the brooder is over-crowded and/or the heat source is too hot.

For this reason, it makes a lot of sense to adapt square-shaped brooder boxes so that the corners are rounded-off. This is easy and cheap to do; even curved sections of stiff card stuck across the corners can be perfectly adequate.

Sourcing the heat

Electricity is the most popular power source for heating brooders, and it's typically used to run light bulbs of one sort or another. The options available offer variations in purchase price (£5+), power output (100-250W) and overall running costs.

Straightforward white-light or infra-red heater bulbs tend to be the most widely used types. Both produce light and heat and, ideally, should be mounted within a specially-made housing that incorporates an effective safety guard to prevent accidental contact between the bulb and anything else.

Usually these sorts of bulb are suspended on a chain so that their height above the birds in the brooder is simple to adjust (to alter the effective heat level within the brooder). However, light-emitting bulbs aren't the only option, and there are breeders who prefer to split the light and heat sources so that they can be controlled independently. Some believe that giving young birds a day/night-type light cycle is an important requirement but, obviously, you can only do this if the lights can be switched off without affecting the heat supply. Having said this, though, I've not had any problems myself with the straightforward, bulb-based set-up; it's worked brilliantly for me over the past 15 years!

If you want to try the separate heat and light source approach, then one option is to buy what's called a dull emitter. Effectively, these are light bulbs that, instead of a clear/pearl envelope, are coated with a ceramic layer; they produce heat but no light. They tend to offer a significantly longer service life than a conventional bulb, and so are correspondingly more expensive. Expect to pay about £12 for each bulb, with power outputs up to 250W.

If you're breeding on a large scale, then it may be worth

Chicks in a brooder must have warmth, dry, clean litter, food, water and a complete absence of drafts. They are extremely vulnerable at this age.

considering a gas-powered brooder heater. These can either be free-standing or suspended, and use Calor gas from a cylinder. They are ideally suited for use in brooder houses without an electrical power supply.

Electric Hen

This slightly scary-sounding device offers another non-light heat source option, utilising a large, flat pad that sits above an area of the brooder pen and is supported on adjustable legs. Modern examples are now covered in a plastic coating, which makes them easy to clean after use.

The idea is that the chicks can move under the heated pad whenever they feel the need for some warmth, much as they would do with a broody hen. Some breeders prefer to use this method, believing that it offers a more 'natural' experience for the chicks. However, it does require more space (to allow the chicks space to move, plus feed and drink away from the heat unit) and, of course, there's still a need for a separate light source.

Electric hens can be bought in varying sizes, but the smallest and most popular measure 18x18in, and can be adjusted on threaded legs up to a maximum height of 10in above the floor of the brooder.

Brooding trouble

The way young birds are reared has a significant affect on both their general health and overall quality once fully grown; it's a vital stage of life that needs to be carefully and correctly managed.

At the most basic level, it's essential that chicks are kept both clean and dry at all times if problems are to be avoided. Overcrowding is also just as important to avoid at this stage, as it is in the birds' later life. None of this is rocket science, but successful management will require attention to detail. One of the fundamentals is to ensure that the chicks never get damp, as this is a serious promoter of disease. Keep an eye on the drinkers in the brooder, making sure that the birds' inevitable clumsiness doesn't cause damp patches to develop in the litter.

This brooder features a heating element (within the wire mesh framework) and a separate bulb providing switchable light.

Plenty of fresh air, but without draughts, is another vital requirement to help guarantee healthy development and minimise the risk of respiratory problems. Consequently, the brooder unit should be placed carefully, in a calm, dry and fresh environment, but out of direct sunlight. It's also wise to keep adult birds out of the way at this stage too, until the chicks have had time to build up some natural immunity. Remember that older birds can be carriers of all sorts of potential trouble, even though they may not be showing any outward signs of illness. Any health 'challenge' faced by vulnerable chicks during the first few weeks of life can prove fatal, so don't take chances.

Diseases

There are too many potential chick-related problems (cerebral hernia, twisted toe, splayed leg, sky-gazing etc.) to detail here, so I'm just going to restrict myself to respiratory trouble; probably the

most common cause for concern anyway among birds of this age.

Respiratory trouble is all too common among young chicks, especially if their keepers are new to the hobby. Fortunately, recognising the danger signs is relatively straightforward, whatever your level of experience. If you spot chicks standing still, with their beaks opening and closing and apparently gasping for breath, then this is a good indicator that all's not well (assuming, of course, that the brooder isn't too hot).

This sort of trouble can be caused in many different ways, but the main culprit is damp and/or dirty bedding. Chicks sleep on the floor and breath in the ammonia produced if the litter is allowed to become contaminated with their droppings. This then damages their sensitive young lungs. Damp litter can promote the production of infectious spores that are potentially harmful to young, vulnerable chicks. Treatment is available from your vet, and can typically be administered via the bird's drinking water. Normally, a product called Terramycin can be prescribed and works both quickly and efficiently.

Coccidiosis

This is another unpleasant condition to watch for. As with respiratory problems, 'coxi' is promoted by generally damp conditions and, once it has developed, it's extremely difficult to clear from your flock – it carries on from year to year, being passed down the generations by contact with infected droppings.

Its presence is usually quite easy to spot because you'll notice blood in the droppings – especially obvious when viewed against clean shavings. There are treatments for this problem but, again, they are prescription-only medicines. Action needs to be swift otherwise fatality rates will be high.

The treatment is normally delivered via the drinking water but, because those suffering can become lethargic (huddled together, standing still and 'droopy'), they may need to be encouraged to drink – you may have to resort to using a syringe. Coccidiosis isn't a pleasant condition, particularly as it can drag chicks down so quickly.

Dietary matters

It's important that the chicks start eating from the moment they get

Chicks must start eating as soon as they get into the brooder, and a nutritionally-balanced chick crumb (left) is the most manageable commercially available feed for them. Switch to growers pellets (right) after about eight weeks.

into the brooder, as their own reserves of energy will be running low by this stage. Always feed a good-quality chick crumb that's fresh and has been supplied by a reputable specialist. This will ensure the birds get all the ingredients needed to get the best start in life.

The physical size of the chick crumb granules makes it easy for the young birds to pick up, swallow and digest. They should be kept on it for around eight weeks, after which then can be switched gradually over to a growers pellet. Continue with this through the rearing period until the birds mature and reach point-of-lay, at

which point you can start feeding them a layers ration.

Mix 'n' match!

As the chicks develop there comes a time when, in some cases, you will have to mix the birds together. If you're faced with this then it's a very good idea to try and ensure that the breeds being put together are compatible, both in terms of age, size and type. Mixing different sizes and ages can and does cause many problems, including bullying and feather pecking (both of which can prove fatal).

Also remember that obvious physical, breed-related differences are likely to cause problems too. For example, crested breeds don't mix well with non-crested types.

Pecking orders

Introducing 'new' birds from the rearing pens to the existing flock can be problematic too. Anything which upsets the existing pecking order within the group is likely to cause a bit of trouble. So adding new birds can be an anxious time when care is needed.

My advice is to add the newcomers after dark, once the rest of the flock is roosting quietly in their house. Carefully place the new birds inside the house, disturbing the residents as little as possible. They should all then emerge in the morning on good terms, although you need to be on hand to keep a wary eye on proceedings!

Get the brooding stage right and you'll give your birds the best chance of growing into healthy, strong adults.

Newly-hatched practicalities

Bob Cross provides some practical advice about successfully looking after newly-hatched chicks

Winter may seem an odd time to be talking about brooding and rearing the coming year's stock – it's not as if you need to start planning well in advance. The three weeks it takes to hatch an egg may seem to offer plenty of time to get things ready.

But, when you're unprepared, this time just flies by.

In the worst case scenario you can find yourself with a batch of day-olds and nowhere really suitable to put them. But start thinking about it now, and you'll be on top of things from the beginning, and have plenty of time to get it right. Apart from that, many breeders mate-up their flocks during October, to brood chicks from December onwards.

Chicks can be hatched during any month, but it's most likely that there is more young breeding stock about at this time of the year, and it's these birds that produce the strongest chicks. Chicks hatched from parents towards the end of the laying season may well be bigger, but they seem to lack some of the vigour.

Brooding preparation

Brooding is the term used to describe the care of chicks in their first 4-6 weeks of life. The time that follows is known as the 'rearing' or 'growing' period. This lasts up to the finishing stage in the case of meat birds, or the onset of laying if the birds are destined for egg production. Chicks can be brooded successfully in large or small numbers, using artificial heat sources or, more naturally, under the supervision of a broody hen. We'll consider both methods later.

There is no set design for brooding accommodation; most poultry houses will suffice and a garden shed is ideal. Sources of light and some method of ventilation are vital factors too, and electricity is desirable if this is the chosen source of energy, although this can be brought in from a nearby building. But whatever building you choose to use, it must be weatherproof, draughtproof and vermin-proof. Another golden rule of brooding is that while a house or shed is in use, it should not be utilised to house any other birds, and should not receive subsequent batches until it's been vacated. Above all, the house must be clean.

So what do I mean by clean? Well, it's certainly not enough simply to remove the previous tenants, clear out the old litter and put in a fresh covering of wood

Houses must be clean, and pressure washers make the best job of driving a jet of water into every nook and cranny.

shavings. All parts of the house, and the used equipment, must be washed. Best results are achieved by embarking on a pre-soak, preferably as soon as possible after

Always use a good disinfectant. The Antec range of products has been developed and tested specially for poultry disease prevention. Cheaper supermarket specials just won't do the job.

the previous litter has been removed. This should be followed by pressure-washing. The jet of water is really effective at cleaning into cracks and corners, and will make a far better job of it than you or I could with a hand-held brush. Having removed the grime, the whole area will need to be disinfected. Use a good disinfectant and buy it from an agricultural supplier. Follow the instructions carefully and be sure to get the dilution correct. The cheap pine-smelling stuff from the supermarket is virtually useless for this job.

Never overlook the disinfecting stage. It's vital that you deal effectively with any risk of contamination that may be present. Remember that day-old chicks are

very susceptible to 'challenges' to their health, and while this stage represents another expense, the cost should be recouped by lower mortality rates and improved quality of the birds being reared. After disinfecting, the house should be left to dry thoroughly. Thereafter, make every effort to keep it that way – don't tramp about inside your wearing your dirty boots!

Setting up

This involves putting all the necessary equipment and materials into the house. Most brooding methods (there are some exceptions) require some form of litter on the floor; the options include white wood shavings,

chopped straw (preferably treated against moulds etc.) and shredded newspaper. These three have been listed in order of my personal preference. The litter should be spread in a layer about 2in (5cm) deep across the whole floor. Then I usually place sheets of paper or cardboard on top of the litter for the first few days, which makes it easier for the chicks to get about, especially the very small breeds. But once the young birds have found their feet, this 'false floor' can be taken out and thrown away.

The brooder itself provides the all-important heat and will either be free-standing on its own legs, or suspended. The important thing is that it is set at an appropriate height, but more about this later. To keep the chicks near to the food, water and heat source, a fence or surround may be useful for the first few days. Surrounds need be no more than about 18in (45cm) high, and can be made from hardboard, small-gauge wire mesh or corrugated paper/cardboard – it's up to you. The photograph below shows one made from galvanised steel. In the past I've made equally successful versions out of the sort of plastic board used for estate agents signs!

Feeders and drinkers will also be needed, and you will need extra of both for the first few days. Artificial lighting is useful too, even where there is a natural source. This will make it easy for you to extend the day-length for

This brooder surround is made from lightweight galvanised steel. Alas, it's no longer available but could be I'm sure, if demand was there. Surrounds can be made from a variety of materials. The brooder sits, or hangs, in the middle.

the first few days of the chicks' life, giving them a better chance of finding all they need and ensuring they get off to a good start.

Essential inputs

A chick, prior to hatching, absorbs what's left of the yolk from inside the egg. This is nature's way of preparing it for its first few days of life in the outside world. In theory this should provide the bird with enough food to see it safely through the first few days of its life. But the reality might be rather different, depending on where your chicks come from. One day's supply will have been used up by the time the chick leaves the incubator, then another may go if it's been transported. That's already half of the reserve gone so, if you're buying-in chicks then it's very important that you make food available immediately.

Consequently, you must provide plenty of feed stations. The food must be accessible, so place it on open trays, shallow dishes or egg trays, for example. Sheets of cardboard work well too because the noise made as the chicks run around on it and peck at the food, attracts and encourages the others to join in. Tube feeder bases and troughs can also be used, filled nearly to the lip. Some food will inevitably be lost into the litter during these early days, but that's better this than losing chicks through starvation. However, while it's important to stress the need to get food into the chicks as a soon as possible, be careful with home-hatched birds – in your haste to feed them, don't remove them from the incubator before they are completely dry and ready.

Chicks should be fed a Chick Starter Crumb, preferably one containing a coccidiostat, which will provide them with a complete and well-balanced diet. This should be fed ad-lib (freely available) until the birds are about eight weeks old. During this initial period, it's also important to make sure all feeders are kept topped up.

In terms of feeder management, the extra feeders that were used at the beginning of the process, should be removed after the first few days. The tubes should be placed on the bases of the others

A tube feeder with the tube removed. The base is used from Day 1, filled nearly to the top. The tube can be refitted once the chicks are feeding well.

when the chicks get to the stage of clearing up the food before they are due to be refilled. If you're using feed troughs then the restricter cover should be put on. To prevent wastage, adjust the tubes (where possible) so that only a small amount of food is showing in the base. Likewise, if troughs are used, keep the feed level low and allow the chicks to clear up before replenishing. As the birds grow, the height of the feeders should be progressively increased so that it remains at about the level of the birds' backs.

Gritty stuff

There are two types of grit; soluble and insoluble. Soluble forms include limestone, oyster shell, cockleshell etc., and contain calcium for bones and eggshells. Where the birds are fed on a starter or grower diet, they won't need additional sources of calcium. In fact, too much can actually cause problems with bone development.

The insoluble types include granite and flint. Both are very hard and are used to help grind the food as part of the digestive process. These grits will also help breakdown straw, wood shavings, grass etc., that are ingested and which may otherwise result in gizzard impaction. It's worth offering flint grit to the birds; at worst it will cost a few pence, but on the plus side it will develop their gizzards, aid digestion and it may save lives.

Grit comes in several sizes – chick, grower and layer. The chick size should be sprinkled on to food once the birds are about one week old, allowing about 1/8oz (3-4g) per chick. This should then be repeated fortnightly, changing to grower size and increasing the amount to 1/3oz (10g) at six weeks.

It can be fed from a separate hopper if you wish. Don't worry if it's not all eaten straight away, it will be over the two weeks. Finally, feeding grit is not essential but is advisable, especially if birds are to be allowed access to pasture. As a rule, it's better to feed grit that's too big rather than too small.

The stuff of life

Water is absolutely vital. A chick can lose all of its fat, half of its protein and still survive. But if it loses just one tenth of its body's moisture content, it will die. It's therefore necessary to ensure that your birds find and drink water as soon as possible after being placed in the brooder. To give chicks the best chance of this I put numerous water points within the surround, so that whichever way the chick walks it will 'bump into' a drinker.

These drinkers include normal water founts, either plastic or galvanised and, for the first week, additional ones (the plastic trays that Mr Kipling apple pies sit on in the box are as good as anything!). If the ring of water at the bottom of the drinker is deep and wide there is the possibility of chicks drowning. To prevent this happening drop some clean pebbles in, or cut a length of hose pipe and put that around the base.

Drinkers need to be raised so that the lip of the drinker is at the chicks' back height, ensuring that the birds find it easy to drink and that less is spilt on to the litter, keeping it as dry as possible. From a hygiene point of view, drinkers will need cleaning every day to remove slime. This forms from the food residue that washes off the birds' beaks as they drink. Clean fresh water must be available at all times.

To check if chicks have found food and/or water on their first night in the brooder, carefully feel the crop. This is the bird's food storage organ and is situated on the breast at the bottom of the throat. The contents should feel like porridge. If they feel hard they have not found water; if it seems too watery then they've not found

additional light close to the brooder, to draw chicks back to the heat. This is particularly important for the first few days, especially when 'dull emitter' infrared lamps or 'electric hens' are being used as the heat source.

After the first few days, once the chicks are nicely settled, lighting is best reduced to natural levels. But if the birds are in a building without windows, then you'll have to continue with artificial light and the 'photo-period' should be about ten hours a day. If infrared lights (either red or white ones) are being used to provide heat, then these will produce light as well, and there's nothing you can do about it.

The early stages are important, and it's possible to make mistakes. Keeping the lighting too bright will increase activity unnecessarily, and might even lead to feather pecking and cannibalism. At the other

Healthy heating

Day-old chicks have no feathers to keep them warm, and they have little ability to regulate their body temperature. Consequently, we must do it for them.

Starting with a temperature of 31°C or so in the brooder on Day 1, this should be gradually reduced by two or three degrees each week, for the first five or six weeks. By the end of this time the chicks will have grown their first feathers, and will be able to control their own temperature. The temperature at the end of the brooding period will ideally be in the region of 18-20°C, although this will vary according to the time of year.

The most difficult decision to make is when to remove the brooder. I've found the best approach is to wean the chicks off it gradually. Start by switching it off during the day, but on again at night. Then start leaving it off at night as well, although leave it in place so they can still sleep under it. Finally remove it altogether, but check the birds carefully to make sure they settle at dusk, and don't pile up and smother. If the forecast is for a cold night then leave the brooder in, or even re-light it. Unfortunately, there really are no hard and fast rules with this one.

Although I've provided reasonably specific temperature figures here, it's still best to use this information as a guide only; far better to rely on the chicks to tell you if things are OK. The signs are fairly obvious. If you find them huddled up under the brooder, with little or no sign of activity, then they are too cold and you'll need to turn up the brooder. Chicks which are panting and spread around away from the brooder are obviously too hot. Finding them all sitting in one corner may well indicate a draught.

Chicks that are contented and comfortable will be evenly spread out within the brooder pen and, if it's light, you should see some that are active and darting around, others that are feeding and drinking plus some that are sleeping. Much can also be learned from the noises being made. Long, drawn-out cheeping indicates a problem while a shorter 'chip, chip' is the talk of happy chicks.

Examples of chick feeders (left) and drinkers (right). These are really only intended for use during the first few days after hatching.

food. Feeling nothing at all is very bad news because it means the poor things have somehow failed to find either water or food, and will be in desperate need of some help.

Brooding conditions

The brooder house should always be well-lit, either naturally, or with artificial lighting, or a combination of the two. Adequate lighting is important because it will enable the chicks to find their way around, and to locate the food and water. It's a good idea to suspend an

extreme, chicks kept in permanently dim conditions, or with day-lengths that are too short, may well not find their food properly, or not have sufficient time to eat it; both can adversely affect growth rates.

In windowed houses where problems with pecking occur, curtains made from sacks, or similar, can be fixed up to reduce the intensity, though make sure that in your efforts to cut down the light, you don't impede ventilation. Alternatively, another solution can be to paint the window glass red.

A common mistake is to keep the house too hot for too long, perhaps in the belief that too hot is better than too cold, but excessive warmth is bad news and will often result in poor feathering and possibly feather pecking. High temperatures also reduce food intake, so growth can be inhibited as well.

Conversely, making the house too cold can be even more of a disaster, promoting chilling which can lead to high mortality. One other point worth remembering is that sudden changes in temperature are sometimes the stimulus for disease.

Sources of heat

Having discussed the requirements in terms of temperature, we ought now to look at some of the ways that heat can be provided.

For small numbers of chicks, electric heating is probably the most convenient. Infrared lamps (either red or white) can be used and these will provide both heat and light. They should be suspended on a lightweight chain, the length of which is reduced by a link every other day or so, thus gradually reducing the temperature. One problem with lamps like these, though, is that if there's a power cut or the bulb blows, the heat source is lost immediately.

An 'electric hen' gives good results, although it looks nothing like a hen! In effect it's an electric blanket mounted in a wooden frame and supported on legs. It's designed so that the chicks can sit underneath with their backs in contact with the warm element. For the first few days it's advisable to use an electric hen in conjunction with a light bulb or infrared lamp suspended nearby, as this will help draw the chicks to the heat. It may also be necessary to put chicks under the 'hen' to show them where to go. Obviously, as the birds grow, the 'hen's' legs need to be extended to maintain the correct height. In the event of a power failure, residual heat is retained under the body of the 'hen' for some time, reducing the risk of losses.

The Brinsea 'Cosy Lamp' is a small electric brooder featuring a canopy under which there's a bulb

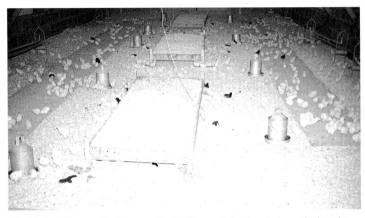

'Electric hens' in use. The tops are filled with wood shavings to keep the heat in and also to help keep them clean. Note the adjustable legs. The rolls of corrugated paper are scattered with feed to ensure the chicks find it. There are no lights hanging by the 'hens' because this house is good and bright.

Infrared brooder lamp fitted with a red bulb.

Infrared brooder lamp (working) with white light. Suspending it with a chain as shown here – rather than a cable – is handy for adjusting the height of the lamp.

providing both heat and light. Something like this is probably best suited where chicks are being reared in very small numbers; they are very cheap to run. What's more,

an added bonus is that it is easy to see that the chicks are indeed inside the brooder.

Other options

Gas brooders are useful, especially where there is no electricity. However, for brooding small numbers this will work out rather expensive. As an example, brooding in a small shed in the summer will require one 49kg gas cylinder, costing about £28. During the winter more will be needed. The other drawback of a gas heater is that it will require servicing, which adds to the expense since that sort of work is best done by a qualified professional. The consequences of cutting corners on maintenance – excessive carbon monoxide production or gas leaks – do not bear thinking about.

There are two types of gas heater commonly used. The first is called an 'open port burner', the second a 'ceramic plaque heater'. The main difference between the two is that the open port burner operates with a visible flame, while the ceramic plaque design simply glows red hot. Most of these designs include a thermostat which can be adjusted a little every day to give the desired temperature reduction. The way that gas brooders work means that they do tend to warm the whole shed, but if they go out there is little or no way of retaining any of this heat.

Paraffin is the third option, and there may still be some of the old 'pyramid hovers' about. Our

Here a small thermostatically-controlled gas brooder is suspended about two feet above white wood shaving litter. Note the number of drinkers and feeders. The board at the back is a hardboard surround. Out of the 250 chicks at day-old, only three died in the first fortnight.

photograph of a pyramid hover (*below*) shows one with chicks that should have long been weaned off heat, but it may give some ideas for making one if you've a mind to. The heat source is a basic oil lamp which is placed centrally under the canopy, beneath a chimney. The heat produced, when combined with the chicks' body heat, is enough to keep them warm. But it's also a good idea to erect a curtain around the outside, which will help keep the heat in and the draughts out.

These are just a few of the heater types that have been used over the years. There is nothing magical about them; anything that will keep the chicks warm, and is safe, will do the job. Of course, a temperature control is a real plus point and running costs are a factor

Paraffin pyramid hover. Under the canopy there's an oil lamp, which is exhausted through the chimney in the centre of the pyramid. This one would appear to have a wire floor.

too. For the more DIY-minded among you, it may be worthwhile making a custom-built brooder at home, and we'll take a look at that in the next chapter of this book.

Good ventilation

Among other things, ventilation offers a supply of fresh air, ensures that stale air is removed and provides important cooling. But, as with heating, there's a balance to be struck. Too much ventilation is a bad thing because it will cause draughts and lower the overall temperature too much.

It's unlikely that any ventilation-related problems will occur when brooding small batches, but they may as the number of birds increases. If attempts are made to keep chicks warm in winter by shutting up all air inlets, the atmosphere will become stuffy and humid. This will detrimentally affect the condition of the litter and, in turn, the health of the birds.

On the other hand, in the summer when the sun gets hot towards midday, the temperature inside a brooder house can rise to stifling levels very quickly, so ventilation needs to be increased to help keep the temperature in check. In my experience it's always better to over- rather than under-ventilate. If too much temperature is lost from the house (within reason, of course) the chicks will

return to the warmth of the brooder, or the heater's thermostat will compensate.

Enough space?

Initially, chicks should be kept within the confines of the brooder surround. But, as they find their way around and increase in size, the space available should be increased. After a week or so the surround should only be rounding-off the corners of the pen, and the space available should be large enough to prevent any risk of crowding or suffocation.

Access to grass runs can be provided once the chicks are strong enough to cope; I would suggest from about two weeks old. Introduce them to this gradually though, and make sure that the grass your young birds are using has been mown short. Allowing them on to areas where it's become long and tough can result in serious digestive problems, and these can prove fatal.

Ensure that they venture out only when they want to; never coerce them. Set up a very small pen around the pop hole so that

Grass like this is very unsuitable for brooding and/or rearing chicks; it must be kept cut or grazed short.

the young birds can easily find their way back inside when they want to. Also, chicks at this stage should only be allowed out on warm, dry days, and need to be closely supervised to start with. For safety and security it's a good idea to make covered runs, starting with a shelter pen. This is a small run (available from gamekeeper suppliers) with an apex construction and clad in flexible, reinforced see-through plastic that provides protection from rain and wind. Once fully-feathered, the birds can be given larger runs that are either open-topped or netted, or they can be allowed to free-range. •

DIY brooder

Making your own brooder is by no means difficult – Terry Beebe reveals the secrets of his own tried and trusted design

A good brooder is important for protecting young chicks at a vital stage in their development. This one is fitted with a red heat/light lamp.

Brooder design is basically quite simple and there are many types on the market today that use a variety of different approaches. Some of them work well, others not quite so well.

Buying ready-made also means you're going to be paying top-dollar and, if you're buying a larger, high-spec. machine, that could equate to £150-200.

A more cost-effective option is to build your own brooder. You'll be able to do it for a fraction of the cost of a ready-made unit, plus it can be built to exactly match your own requirements. I find that the use of an enclosed brooder unit has its own major advantages, both for the rearing and also the guaranteed survival of the chicks. The brooder that's featured here *(see page 55 for plan)* was built to my own design, and has been working brilliantly for me over the past seven years.

It was designed specifically with the intention of being easy to use and simple to maintain. What's more, the results it's produced ever since it's been running have been superb. I've based the construction details included here to produce a unit the same size as mine, and using all-new materials. However, the dimensions can all be adjusted to produce a brooder of whatever size best suits your own needs. Also, if you prefer, it's perfectly possible

to achieve great results using secondhand materials, and to save a lot of cash in the process.

As things stand, I've worked out the dimensions of this brooder so that standard-sized sheets of plywood will suffice with little wastage. In all, you'll need four sheets of 8x4 ply to complete the

job. The thickness you use really is a matter of personal preference but, for mine, I worked with half-inch sheet. Although this is heavier to handle, it certainly creates a strong and stable finished result.

The plans reproduced here show all the important dimensions (in millimetres) and, if you follow them

Hinged doors on the front of the brooder provide excellent access and can feature mesh or Perspex inspection windows. The doors are hinged on the top panels.

carefully, you'll find it easy to prepare and assemble the unit. The main diagram and picture show the brooder with both the top doors closed; these access points have been fitted with wire mesh inserts but you can use clear Perspex to create a window effect. Whichever you opt for, however, the idea is to provide an easy way for you to observe the chicks inside, without causing them any disturbance. They're also large enough to provide good access to the inside of the unit, which is an important factor both in everyday use (providing feed and water) and for maintenance and cleaning purposes.

You should cut the sheets of plywood as shown in the diagram. Make sure, when cutting the first one, that both the 'ends' match, and that the other two sections (labelled 'top') are cut and retained to form the fixed top of the brooder. The front of the unit is not as high as the rear, allowing the fitting of the large, hinged doors at a convenient angle.

My preference is to use an internal timber frame for additional strength, and to provide a convenient fixing for the ply sheet. I also extended it down to provide integral legs for the unit. However, if you prefer, you can simply screw the ply together without the need for a frame at all, although this won't produce such a strong and stable result in my view.

The frame which extends up and over the top of the brooder is there to support the two heat lamps, the flex and chain for which hangs down and through cut holes at each end of the top panel. Hooks are screwed into the frame above to provide anchorage for the chain, and to provide a simple way of adjusting the height of the lamps.

The holes cut in the top panels need to be large enough to allow the heat lamp units to be lowered through, so the actual size will be determined by the type of lamp being used. A jig saw makes quick work of cutting these important access points. Also remember that the hinges for the opening front doors need to be mounted on the front edge of the top panel.

Fitting the doors should be a straightforward business, assuming you've got the sizes right! Add a

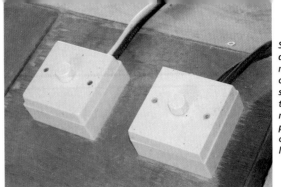

Simple domestic dimmer switches make lamp heat control much simpler than the traditional method of physically raising or lowering the light unit.

small pull handle to the base of each so they're easy to use. The mesh in the door can be whatever size you prefer – my own unit has a sliding Perspex window which is useful in extremely cold conditions.

One other important structural addition is the central divider. This means that, in the eight-foot model detailed here, there's enough space to create two separate brooder compartments inside if required. You can use one lamp for each section, or have the whole interior opened up into one large compartment heated by two lamps.

The diagram illustrates a divider made from a very fine weld mesh, which is quite a good option, though you may choose to make yours of solid wood, as I did.

Finally, in the plan view looking straight down into the brooder interiors, you'll notice that the corners have been rounded-off. This is done by bending and fastening pieces of hardboard sheet across the corners, and the purpose is to eliminate the risk of chick suffocation. Leaving the corners straight-edged means there's a chance that, in a crowded brooder, a young bird can get trapped and smothered in the corner. I've

learned this through bitter experience. Rounding-off the corners in this simple way prevents it from happening altogether.

Red hot
I've only ever used the red glass heat lamps – which supplies both heat and light at the same time – in my chick brooders. These bulbs are readily available from all good poultry supply outlets, and come in varying ratings between 100W and 250W. The lamp units themselves are normally supplied complete with hanging chain and cable, ready for use. Traditionally the heat level for the birds is adjusted simply by varying the height of the lamp, but I've taken a slightly more modern approach by fitting domestic dimmer switches to my unit. These aren't expensive and offer more control as far as temperature is concerned.

If you prefer the dull emitter (heat without light) option, lamps of this sort can also be used with this brooder design, but you'll have to add an additional, conventional light fitting as well. Chicks need light to survive, but a low wattage energy-saver bulb will be perfectly adequate, and should keep running costs to a minimum too. •

The holes in the top panels need to be large enough to allow through the light unit. Modern reflector designs are smaller, so the holes won't need to be as large as the one seen here.

DIY double brooder

The plans here will make the eight-foot, twin-compartment brooder seen on the opening page of this chapter. Dimensions can be scaled to whatever suits you best.

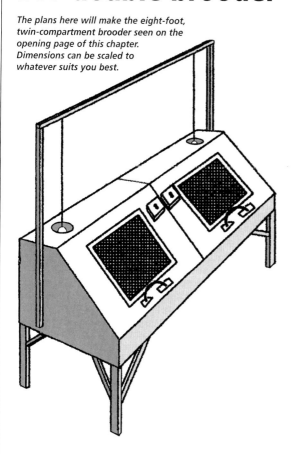

Materials

4 sheets of exterior ply 2,400mm x 1,200mm
29.2m x 35mmx35mm timber framing
5.3m x35mmx35mm for timber legs
3x square-metre sheets 25mm x 25mm weldmesh
1 sheet 2,400mm x 600mm hardboard
0.5kilo 35mm galvanised nails
1m single link chain
2 heatlamps with shades
2 electric light switches
2 cupboard handles
4 hinges

Layout for cutting

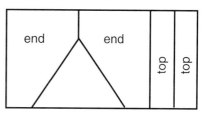

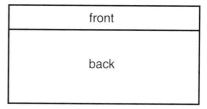

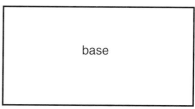

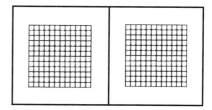

sloping top

Endpieces

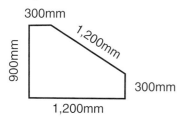

Interior from above

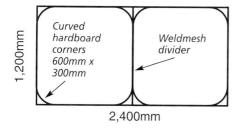

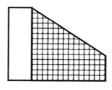

Central partition
25mm x 25mm mesh

Health chick

Bob Cross investigates some of the most common ailments that can affect young and growing stock

It would be nice to think we could rear all the chicks we hatch; sadly this is rarely the case as, even under ideal conditions and despite perfect management, some simply won't make it.

Many disorders can affect poultry, so it's worthwhile looking at a number of the conditions that can cause problems during the early stages of poultry development.

The first point to note is that strict hygiene and effective levels of bio-security will keep many diseases at bay. What's more, when this is backed-up with vaccination and in-feed medication, losses from infectious diseases can be minimised in many instances. However, bird health can be compromised in plenty of other ways.

Splayed legs or 'spraddles'

These terms are fairly descriptive of the symptoms presented by this unfortunate condition. Splayed legs are usually seen in young chicks as they are taken from the hatch tray, especially so if their removal from the incubator

Splayed legs; this gosling's legs are spread sideways, making it unable to stand and walk.

has been delayed. Goslings and turkey poults seem particularly vulnerable, appearing weak on their legs. In extreme cases the legs fold out sideways, making it impossible for the hatchling to walk.

Treatment is simple and usually effective; the legs are 'hobbled' by tying them loosely together with soft string, thus restricting the sideways movement. The specific cause of this condition is uncertain, but it seems to be more prevalent where chicks are kept in the incubator longer than

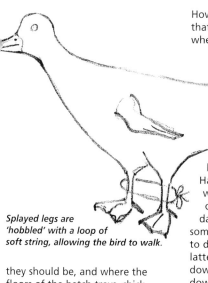

Splayed legs are 'hobbled' with a loop of soft string, allowing the bird to walk.

they should be, and where the floors of the hatch trays, chick boxes and pens are smooth and slippery. Preventative measures include covering the floor of the hatch tray with clean hessian, or other similarly textured and air-porous material, so that the young birds are ensured a good grip underfoot. Similar materials can be used in the chick boxes and, providing at least 5cm (2in) of litter material in the brooder house will also enable the chick to get a good toehold, thus reducing the incidence in the latter stages.

Toe troubles
While 'curled toe paralysis' and 'crooked toe syndrome' may sound like similar problems, they are actually two distinct diseases with unrelated causes.

Curled toe paralysis is the result of feeding diets deficient in Vitamin B2 (Riboflavin). Affected chicks are usually 2-3 weeks old, and will be seen to crouch on their hocks and will be reluctant to move. The toes turn inwards and under the foot – fist-like – and, when forced to move, the young birds do so either by walking on the outer side of the feet, or by propelling themselves along on their hocks.

In the early stages, the chicks will appear to be in good condition but, if left untreated, they will quickly become reluctant to move, feed and drink. They will simply lie on their sides, waste away and die. Thankfully, though, this problem should be a rarity for birds fed on properly-formulated rations.

However, it's worth bearing in mind that the condition can appear where diets are diluted with other food stuffs, or if stale or mouldy food is being fed.

If breeding stock go short of riboflavin, it'll not only be leg problems that you'll have to worry about. Hatchability will be reduced too, with much embryonic mortality occurring around the twelfth day of incubation, although some chicks continue to develop up to day 20. Those dying at this latter stage will display 'clubbed down'; brought about by the down failing to rupture the follicle, and continuing to grow within – the name adequately describes the signs.

Where a hatch has been lower than expected and these symptoms have featured, vitamin supplements should be given to the surviving chicks as they are likely candidates for curled toe paralysis and, similarly, to the parents to prevent problems in future hatches. Also, administering vitamins to those already suffering will do much to effect a cure. Storing food in a cool dry place, and using it before its 'best before' date should ensure that the vitamin content remains intact.

It's also worth noting that the vitamin is also present in the chicks' droppings and, as a result of bacterial action, the content increases over time (days rather than weeks). The lessons to be learned here are, firstly, that this problem is less likely to occur in litter-reared flocks. Secondly, the litter should be allowed to develop, rather than be removed on a daily basis, so that the chicks may glean part of their requirement from this source.

Crooked toe syndrome
This condition is similar to curled toe paralysis in the early stages but, as it develops the difference becomes apparent; the toes curl sideways only. The foot doesn't become fist-like, the chick doesn't use its hocks for walking and, unlike curled toe paralysis, this

problem doesn't appear to affect overall growth.

The precise cause of the condition is unclear; it seems more prevalent where bright, infra-red lamps are used as a brooding heat source, especially where these are combined with solid floors and minimal litter material. This brooding method provides the chicks with constant light, allowing them to feed 24 hours a day and causing them to grow faster and heavier than they would otherwise do. This alone may be the fundamental cause of the problem. Now the good news! This condition is reversible to a great extent. When the heat lamps are removed after four or five weeks, the 'day length' is shortened, feed intake is reduced, growth rate slows down and the toes start to get better. Most sufferers will have fully recovered by the eight-week mark.

Using an alternative heat source for brooding should help prevent crooked toe syndrom in the first place. If this isn't possible, then make sure the youngsters get plenty of litter on the floor. Removing feed troughs overnight will also help to slow the growth rate down. If you find that certain strains appear more susceptible than others, it may be assumed to be an inherited fault. In this case it's important to identify the birds responsible for passing on the trait and remove them from the breeding program.

Slipped tendon (Perosis)
This is a deformity of the leg bones. The hock joint of affected birds will become greatly enlarged and, if studied closely, the upper end of the metatarsus (the scale-covered leg bone) and the lower part of the tibia (the bone immediately above the hock joint), will be found to be twisted. As a result, the Achilles' tendon slips out of the groove at the back of the hock joint. Once this has happened, the tendon remains taut, pulling the leg backwards and sideways. One or both legs may be affected and, in the latter case, the bird will only be able to walk on its hocks.

There are various factors responsible for perosis; mineral and vitamin deficiencies will give rise to the condition, especially if

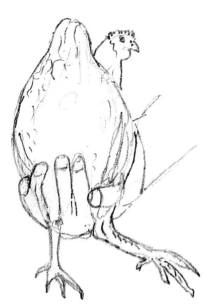

Perosis, affecting the bird's right leg. Note how the leg is twisted, pulled backwards and sideways.

manganese and choline are lacking. Similarly, excesses of some may effect the availability of others. For example, an excess of calcium will effect the utilisation of manganese. Genetics too may play their part; certain strains behave differently in their utilisation and, therefore, requirements of these nutrients, thus making them more susceptible to the condition than others.

Perosis is less likely to occur if a complete and balanced diet is fed, and one that is designed for the type of stock receiving it. High-density feeds that tend to force growth should be avoided as these may stimulate the condition in any strains predisposed to it. Should slipped tendons appear to run in a particular family, steps should be taken to identify carriers and eliminate them from the breeding program.

If a balanced diet is fed, and steady rather than fast growth is the aim, it's unlikely that perosis will be a problem. Only insoluble grit (flint or granite) should be given during the growing period, to prevent upsetting the mineral balance present in the compound ration.

Treatment is unlikely to be effective. The tendon can be relocated into its groove but, because the bones are twisted, alignment will be poor and it will slip out again the moment the leg is flexed. Casualties should be euthanased as soon as possible, to prevent unnecessary suffering.

Injuries and infections

Lameness can result from injury, caused by thorn punctures in the foot which subsequently become infected. When this happens the affected foot will feel hot to the touch, and usually contains pus. Close inspection will reveal the entry point, from which the causal object can be removed and the purulent matter squeezed out. The

Bumblefoot; typically showing a large abscess between the toes.

wound should be washed with antiseptic and the bird placed in clean quarters until recovered.

It's possible that the wound will heal on its own without human intervention, but it's also possible that the infection will spread up the leg to the hock joint, turning this arthritic and rendering the bird useless. If first aid remedies don't work and the hock joint appears inflamed, seek veterinary help for antibiotic treatment as soon as possible.

Marek's disease

The virus involved with this disease gives rise to tumours around the body – liver, spleen, kidneys, lungs, ovary, muscle, eyes, nerves etc. The disease normally affects birds between three and six months old, often appearing in flocks as they come into lay. Female birds seem to be more susceptible.

'Fowl/range paralysis', as it used to be called, is probably the best known, and these names are particularly apt when the nerves in the legs and wings are involved.

Lameness is the first sign; the wings also droop and it rapidly gets worse. In a few days the bird is incapacitated and lays on its side with one leg stretched forward and the other one backwards. This type of Marek's disease can be identified fairly easily by observation, but there are others for which the symptoms are internal, so only visible upon post-mortem examination and then to a trained eye. In these latter types the only symptoms may be wasting and mortality. Some breeds and strains are very susceptible to the disease, while

Fowl paralysis (Marek's disease) in its early stages, when the bird displays weakness, unsteady gait and drooping wing.

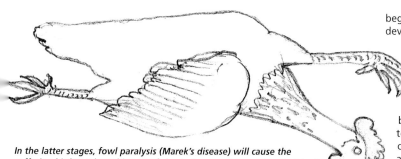

In the latter stages, fowl paralysis (Marek's disease) will cause the suffering bird to adopt this sort of classical pose, with one leg stretched out forwards, and the other one backwards.

others appear quite resistant. In those that are susceptible mortality will be high, but a resistant strain might only suffer the odd loss.

It's important to get professional help to confirm diagnosis and provide advice regarding future husbandry techniques. There is no treatment; casualties should be killed as they are found. Fortunately, there are vaccines available which prevent the signs of the disease developing, and these are administered at day-old, before chicks enter the brooder house. However, even though these vaccines are very successful, they should not be regarded as an alternative to good hygiene.

The virus lives in dust, especially that derived from feathers. It can remain active for up to a year, so it's vital that houses are thoroughly cleaned and disinfected before chicks are placed. If vaccination is not considered an option and Marek's is known to cause problems on the site, the chicks must be reared elsewhere for at least the first month of their lives.

Laying troubles

Having managed to guide our birds to the point of lay in a fit and healthy state, it would be great to think that the worst is behind us. In most cases it will be but there are one or two other problems which it's as well to be aware of as hens come into lay.

The first of these is prolapse of the oviduct, which is often seen in pullet flocks as they commence lay. It may be caused by straining too hard to pass an egg that's too simply too big. The unpleasant upshot is that the bird pushes the end of the oviduct and cloaca out through its vent.

The problem is easy to spot by the reddish, fleshy mass that's visible around the outside of the vent. The condition isn't infectious, although multiple cases may arise if the necessary conditions prevail. Of more concern, however, is the fact that it may promote cannibalistic tendencies among the other birds. Treatment may be attempted but, to stand any chance of success, the casualty must be removed from the flock immediately. The protruding parts are washed in antiseptic solution and gently pushed back inside, with fingers smeared liberally with zinc ointment.

Delaying this action will result in bacterial contamination from litter and house dust, and from other birds pecking at the wound. This in turn may lead to peritonitis and death. If an egg is trapped an attempt can be made to remove it, but if any tissue is torn the bird must be killed straight away.

Having administered first aid, the bird should be placed in a clean coop to recover, and must be fed a light diet – something that will pass easily through the system and doesn't encourage laying. Unfortunately, reoccurrence is likely when the next egg is laid so, unless the bird is of particular value, it may be as well to kill it and prevent further suffering.

Ensuring that pullets are well grown before lay will help reduce the incidence of prolapse, with emphasis on correct feeding and lighting control to achieve this. Replacement pullets should be fed a diet sufficient to allow them to grow well and develop a fit but not fat body. Rearing on an increasing plane of light – one where the day length is increased with age – will cause precociousness and laying will

begin in a body that's not yet developed enough to cope with it. Once in lay, it's important not to over-stimulate pullets with light as this is likely to lead to double-yolked eggs, which the bird will find difficult to pass. Rearing birds outside makes it difficult to control the light. If this is the chosen method, it's better to avoid rearing where the growing period coincides solely with increasing day lengths. For the same reason, bought-in point-of-lay pullets – especially those light, hybrid types – are best not housed during the summer months.

Egg peritonitis

This condition refers to an inflammation of the lining of the abdominal cavity. Blockages in the oviduct, ruptures in its wall or that of the intestine may be responsible. Likewise, yolk material entering the abdomen rather than the oviduct, or bacterial contamination as a result of a prolapse, also give rise to this problem. In acute cases the bacteria multiply rapidly, septicaemia sets in and the bird dies.

Regrettably there's no cure and, while little can be done about tears in the intestine or the oviduct, much can be done with regard to the other causes. Certain diseases, in particular Infectious bronchitis, damage the reproductive tract and thus increasing the likelihood of yolks entering the abdomen and setting up infection. Strict hygiene standards and vaccination should help reduce the incidence of the condition by this cause. Rough handling of birds, especially those at point-of-lay and in full lay, is likely to increase the chances of yolks going astray inside the bird. Prevention is simple; they should be handled with the greatest care and consideration.

Although the ailments I've described here aren't going to be responsible for great losses, there's nothing worse than losing good stock due to easily preventable problems. With a bit of common sense, plus effective husbandry practices and good management, health will be maintained and the birds should all meet your expectations.

Hatching under hens

Andy Marshall looks at natural brooding, with an introduction to the practical requirements for getting started

Natural incubation – using a hen to hatch a clutch of eggs – is very rewarding for the small poultry keeper. It doesn't matter if you keep bantams, large fowl, ducks, turkeys or geese; all will safely hatch their offspring providing some basic rules are followed.

The first thing to bear in mind is that there's nothing new about natural incubation – 100 years ago most eggs would have been hatched naturally. Fifty years ago most game birds were hatched naturally and, today, most ornamental waterfowl breeders still rely heavily on broodies to hatch very valuable, and often rare, stock. But it's not just the waterfowl breeders who use

Natural brooding can be very rewarding, as long as you've got the time necessary to make sure everything runs smoothly.

broodies, keepers of endangered pheasants will also prefer a broody bird to the services of an incubator. This choice overcomes all the humidity problems associated with the use of modern incubators, plus there are other important maternal benefits too. The hen can teach the tiny young chicks or ducklings how to eat, as well as calm them down by not being nervous when in close contact with humans.

If you think you want to try natural incubation, then there are a series of requirements that you must be able to satisfy before you can even consider 'sitting a broody'. As with most aspects of poultry keeping, attention to detail and maintaining a routine are both absolutely crucial factors if you don't want to end up with broken eggs, the broody deserting the nest or, worse still, eating the chicks as they hatch.

So while there's real satisfaction to be gained from rearing chicks 'as nature intended', there are potential dangers too. You'd be wrong to assume that, just because it's a natural process, you can simply leave the bird to get on with it.

To be successful, the whole process needs to be managed; you must be vigilant, and understand the different requirements at each stage of the incubation and hatching sequence.

So, to avoid disappointment, here are the requirements.

Care and attention

Do you have the time? You must be prepared to deal with a broody at the same time, every day, during the whole incubation period. In addition, you'll need to maintain careful supervision for the first few days after hatching, to ensure that all remains well. You will need to set aside 20-30 minutes each day so that the broody can be allowed off the nest to eat, drink and defecate. Normally it makes sense to combine this with other jobs so that you lift her off, go and feed your other birds, for example, then come back and replace her on the nest. The broody won't need to be supervised while she's off the nest, but you need to lift her off in the first place.

Equipment

To do the job properly you will need to buy (or build yourself) what's called a sitting box, where the broody hen incubates the eggs. Also, you'll need a broody coop and run for the hen and chicks to use after hatching.

It's also important to set aside an area where the broody can eat and drink during her 20-30-minute daily

A well-designed and well-made broody coop with attached run.

A front-opening door makes life in the sitting box much easier for bird and keeper.

break when she is off the nest. Ideally, this is normally an enclosed run so that it's easy to catch her and return her to the nest.

For the novice I do not recommend allowing the broody to have sight of her eggs when she's off the nest. If she spots them she'll be unlikely to settle to feeding and drinking because the desire to get back will be strong. This is why the sitting box is so handy; it can be closed once she's out and it won't be possible to see the eggs at all.

Isolation

Do not allow the broody to continue to sit in the same house where she is kept normally. Other hens will lay where she is sitting, resulting in different dates for hatching, plus she will be disturbed and the risk of her deserting the nest is increased. Also, the eggs will develop at different rates, so you'll end up with a staggered hatch, which is bad news. If this happens the hen will want to leave the nest with the first hatched, leaving the other eggs completely. In addition, the broody could be bullied when she comes off the nest by the other birds in the pen, which also increases the risk of desertion.

The right breed?

Are your birds a breed or strain that is sufficiently docile to sit naturally? All chickens *could* go broody, but not all will. Neither will all of them be prepared to sit for the required length of time. It's all a matter of breeding.

You need to know that the bird

will be reliable and sit for the full term. Most utility or heavy breeds will do this very easily, as well as some of the lighter breeds including Scots Greys and Old English Game. With these latter two, though, be careful when a bird is thinking about going broody, as both Scots Grey and Old English Game males tend to become very protective. Generally, light breeds only go broody sometimes and are not nearly so reliable. Breeds originating from the Mediterranean region are also unlikely to make good and reliable broodies.

Some of the best-known 'broody' pure breeds include Sumatra Game, Silkies and Yokohamas. Silkies are famous for going broody frequently, and at all times of the year, plus they are extremely reliable. However, it's also worth noting that if you intend using pure-bred Silkies, their fine plumage can cause problems for newly-hatched chicks. The risk is that the young birds might become entangled, even to the point of strangulation. Silkie crosses are very popular, and I have several friends who cross Silkies with Marans or Light Sussex bantams, to produce perfect broodies. Other popular crosses, or pure breeds, include Plymouth Rock and Wyandotte bantams. A gamekeeper friend of mine would cross a Maran bantam cock with large Silkie females to hatch his partridge chicks. The resulting cross produced normally-feathered females that weren't so big that they'd crush the partridge eggs, and had very strong broody tendencies. This was just what he wanted as he also kept ornamental pheasants. With some types of pheasant, having broodies available in mid-winter was a major plus.

Breeds such as Sussex, Cochin, Brahma, Rhode Island Red, Orpington, and Wyandottes will all make good, reliable broodies.

Some true bantams such as Pekins and Belgians can make fine mothers but, as with Silkies, the foot feathers on Pekins can be a problem unless trimmed before sitting.

Today's modern hybrids have had the broody trait selected out, so any that might happen to go broody may not be so reliable to sit full time and rear the young – they do not make suitable broodies.

Waterfowl and turkeys

In my experience most breeds of duck will sit, although I've only ever allowed Black East Indians and Call Ducks to rear their own ducklings. Providing the mother duck is tame and trusts you, they make great mothers. I have heard that other breeds will sit and rear their own ducklings, but to the novice this can be fraught with danger. Timid birds may desert the eggs at the drop of a hat, while others might prove clumsy and break the eggs.

Geese, on the other hand, generally make perfect mothers, although there are a few golden rules to be followed. When a goose decides to go broody, mark the eggs with a clear cross and then collect any fresh eggs that are laid by the pen mates. Then decide if you are going to leave the other geese in the pen or move them elsewhere. Leaving them will mean that the non-broody birds will continue to lay in the nest, causing the sitting goose hassle. There will also be eggs in different stages of development.

Also, remember that ganders can be fiercely protective of a sitting goose, so be careful especially if you have young children. When you want the goose to sit, give her fresh eggs that have not been sat on and remove all the others.

It's a similar story with turkey breeds. Most will go broody and rear their own poults very well. Make sure the eggs are all the same age and, if possible, leave the

turkey hen undisturbed. It is essential to give the sitting turkey (duck or goose) peace and quiet.

Checking for parasite infestations

Is the broody free from lice, mite and scaly leg? Curing the mite and lice can be done at the beginning of incubation. Failure to do so increases the risk of desertion. If the bird has scaly leg, then this will be transferred to the baby chicks. So a broody suffering in this way has to be rejected until the problem has cleared up because scaly leg is so very infectious. Providing that

Broodies need to be thoroughly treated with lice powder before they are allowed to start sitting.

lice and mite are dealt with at the beginning, the broody should be fine. These two parasites are a common cause of desertion after day 10-15 simply because the bird cannot stay still any longer with the constant itch!

Encouraging broodiness

This is quite easy during the late spring months, but perseverance is

important if you are looking for winter or early-spring broodies. Some people develop their own strain of broodies based on Silkie or Sussex crosses. Others have specific birds which they know will go broody if encouraged.

Hens lay eggs in clutches, which can be anything from six to 12 in number, before having a rest for a day or so. If you leave 6-8 pot eggs, small round stones, golf balls or even lumps of coal in the nest box, you'll encourage the hens to go broody. But don't leave real eggs in the box because some could get broken and encourag egg-eating. Using 'dummies' also avoids the problem of dirty or stale eggs.

At the same time, give the birds a small amount of maize in their feed ration. Be careful not to add too much though, as maize encourages fat production which, in laying birds, can promote prolapse.

When can you be sure that the bird is actually broody? There are a number of characteristic, tell-tale signs to watch out for.

Within two or three weeks you will start to notice a hen spending more time in the nest box. The hen should shuffle her wings when a hand is placed under her, with the fingers uppermost. She should also draw eggs underneath her, using her beak, ruffle her neck and body feathers, and have a bare hot breast with no feathers. Finally, she will make a distinctive 'clocking' noise; this is what gave rise to broody hens traditionally being known as 'clockers'.

If the bird is genuinely broody

You can tell when a hen goes broody by her reaction to being moved.

A bare patch of skin on the breast is a classic sign of a broody hen.

It's sensible to run broodies 'in tandem', just in case one of them goes off the idea!

and you lift her off the nest, she'll ruffle her feathers and just sit there making that clucking noise. Also, when she's feeding she'll start to call to imaginary chicks, or maybe simply take great lumps out of your hand! All of these signs are good indicators that the bird is truly broody.

Other tell-tale signs include a tendency for the hen to raise her back feathers, spread her wings and make an almost aggressive clucking sound when she's placed on the ground. The final confirmation will be whether or not the hen stays sitting tight in the nest box on the false eggs in the evening. If she does, then she's probably broody.

Sitting comfortably?

Where you sit a broody is a major factor in terms of success or failure. Remember that, under natural conditions, a broody hen will seek out a quiet place away from the rest of the flock where she can have peace and quiet. So by all means site the sitting box outside, but not in the main chicken run, and of course it needs to be in a fox-free environment. Also take care to keep it out of direct sunlight as it can become very hot in sunny weather.

Since the box is outside, you can make a good, deep nest using straw straight on the ground (no box floor). Some people recommend that you make a nest shape with soil and then line it with straw. This is to ensure the eggs stay in the nest and to provide moisture for them. I find a good deep straw nest straight on the ground is fine. Being on the ground is important as this will provide moisture for the eggs during incubation.

If an outside sitting box isn't possible or isn't safe, then an empty garden shed is fine, but make sure

you place a soil base under the nest, and ensure that it is slightly damp before putting the straw on top. If you don't have a proper sitting box, then you can use an old-fashioned wooden orange box, or even a sturdy cardboard one, though if you've never sat a broody before I would not recommend the cardboard box approach.

Take the broody from her pen when it's dark, and dust her with flea and lice powder. This is very important as external parasites can cause the hen to desert during incubation, which is the last thing you want. After a thorough dusting, place her on the false eggs she has been sitting on in the nest box, close it up and leave her there. She will either settle down, clucking, on the eggs straight away, or take a little time to adjust.

Don't forget that she'll need to be fed and watered once a day. So either the next morning or evening

– whichever suits your routine best – lift her off for her daily exercise and feed. If you find her standing up, and the nest is all over the place, then she's not broody and will need to be returned to the main pen. But, hopefully, you'll find her sitting snugly on the nest, and you'll notice that she raises her feathers as you lift the lid of the box.

Allow her 20-30 minutes exercise to feed, drink and defecate. She should be fed with straight wheat and drink fresh water. There must also be access to grit if she wants it. Also, giving her the opportunity for a dust bath is recommended.

Make sure she does defecate before returning to the nest, to avoid nest-fouling. If fouling does happen, carefully remove the dirty nest material and replace it with fresh. Remember, also, that the eggs can be broken if the broody is unsettled or handled roughly. Allow her to walk naturally back to on to

If a hen is unreliable as a broody, she may suddenly trash the nest, as has happened here on the left.

the nest – good sitting box design can assist this. However, if an egg does get broken, you must carefully remove every last trace otherwise the hen may be encouraged to eat the remaining eggs.

I tend to get the hen into a proper sitting routine before giving her the hatching eggs. This can take anything between two and seven days, but it's worth it. I always want to be confident that she's a definite sitter before giving her the eggs. Too often beginners are impatient and are then disappointed when the hen deserts part way through.

Egg management

Once your broody hen is settled into her daily routine, and you know that she is going to be a reliable sitter, then it's time to start thinking about the eggs you're going to introduce. Obviously these must be fertile, but it's also vital that they are all at least 24 hours old. The germ cell inside each egg must be left dormant before sitting begins. If this doesn't happen then the likely result will be a batch of eggs that all hatch at different times, which is bad news. Ideally you want all the hatching to take place around about the same time because if any chicks arrive appreciably before the rest, the hen is likely to lose interest in the remaining unhatched eggs, and leave the nest.

Hatching eggs need to be kept in a cool dry place, but the way in which this is done depends on the type of egg. For example, waterfowl and pheasant breeders (especially of the rarer types) tend to use trays of sand; storing the eggs on their sides and turning them every day until they are needed for a sitting.

For best hatching results use eggs that have been stored for 7-10 days. Fertility and hatchability tend to drop off sharply after 10 days. Store your eggs pointed end up in trays which are slightly tilted at one end and turn periodically during each day before setting in incubator pointed end down.

If you are sitting eggs in frosty weather, you may have to collect them more regularly than once a day to prevent the germ from dying. Make sure the nest boxes are kept clean and that, for

As chicks hatch, make sure that all broken shell sections are removed – larger sections can impede the hatching of other eggs.

BROODING BOXES

The quality of the equipment you use can make a big difference to the end result. I've spent a lot of time researching sources and the best I've found is M&D Animal Housing, of Fareham, Hants. (tel: 01489 798383, www.animalhousing.biz). M&D kindly provided the equipment featured here, and can be thoroughly recommended.

The sitting box featured is a 'double', allowing two broodies to sit at one time. This is a good idea as you've always got a reserve in case of problems. I especially like M&D's design; the roof lifts up allowing for inspection and checking, but it also has the access door at the front for letting the bird in and out. In this way you can simply drop the front flap so that the broody, on seeing her eggs, will walk in happily and settle back on to her clutch.

The broody coop is an excellent design as well. Other companies sell a combined run and coop unit but, personally, I prefer having the two items as separate entities; it offers much more flexibility. As with the sitting box, the coop features a lift-up roof, and there's a barred front on a hinged frame, which can be opened a week after hatching – by this time the chicks will be nice and sturdy on their feet. Simple turn buttons hold the front flap in place and this, in turn, can double-up as a sunshade on top of the run in hot weather.

waterfowl, the birds have plenty of floor litter. I prefer wood shavings to straw for keeping the eggs clean. It's also advisable to wash the eggs in a proprietary disinfectant before sitting. Dirty eggs can suffer from bacterial infections which are capable of penetrating the shell and killing the developing embryo inside.

Once you're ready to go, replace the pot eggs that the broody has been sitting on, with the real ones. Do this while she's off the nest having her daily 20-30-minute feed. The size of the clutch depends very much on the size of the broody hen. As a guide, a bantam will be happy to sit on 5-10 bantam eggs, depending on the breed, while a

Sitting hens need 20-30 minutes off the nest each day.

large fowl hen should manage about 12 large eggs. If you are sitting waterfowl eggs under a large hen, then work on the basis of up to 10 duck eggs or 4-6 goose eggs. It's a matter of judgement really. If you can see the eggs through the bird's feathers when she's sitting, then there are too many and some should be removed. The broody herself moves the eggs from the outside to the inside of the nest every day, to ensure even incubation.

As far as time-scale is concerned, chicken eggs take 21 days to hatch, and waterfowl 28 days, subject to variety.

Whether or not to moisten the eggs before hatching is another area of debate. If the sitting box has no floor then usually there's no need to do this because the sitting hen will draw moisture up from the ground. But if the box has a floor, or is located inside a shed, then the eggs should have warm (blood-heat) water sprinkled on to them on days 16, 17 and 18 for bantams, or days 18, 19 and 20 for large fowl. Waterfowl eggs require more and this procedure should be carried out from day 20 to 27. Do this literally just before the hen returns to the nest, otherwise you risk chilling the eggs. Just a couple of drops on each egg will do. I use a cereal bowl that I put my fingers in and then dribble the water over the eggs.

The big day

When it comes to hatching day, keep disturbance to a minimum. Check the hen and gently lift her off the eggs to have a look (take care in case chicks are under her wings). If most of the eggs have hatched, cover the nest with a flannel to keep the chicks warm and not calling, which will distract the hen when she is having her daily feed. Normally she will be very quick and want to get back to her brood. Remove all the egg shells to ensure that a hatched egg does not encase an unhatched one.

Eggs that have started hatching need to be taken out of the nest as the hen returns, to avoid them being broken. Then, once she's in place, carefully replace the egg underneath. Do this by holding the egg so that it's shielded in your

Chicks should be allowed access to a small run like this, but don't allow the hen in there for the first week.

hand – to prevent her from pecking at it as it's replaced. Then leave the hen undisturbed. If you feed during the morning, then check her again in the early evening to see how things are progressing, but don't lift her off completely. Remove any shells. If you feed in the evening, then check her in the morning.

If all is well and the chicks have fluffed up, transfer them and the hen to a broody coop and run. The same applies for waterfowl. Any eggs that don't hatch should be disposed of.

Avoid trouble

If the hen is unsettled by fleas or lice, or disturbed by other poultry, she can tread on the hatching eggs and kill the chicks. Some hens will even kill and eat the chicks as they hatch. This can be a particular problem when there's plumage mismatch – for example, if you have a brown-feathered hen hatching black chicks, or vice versa. So do be careful.

Hatching success rates should be pretty high under a broody. Chicks finding it difficult to break out will be a rarity, as will cases of 'dead in the shell'. However, if you do find problems like this, check through

your hatching routine since this is more likely to be the problem. Another common cause of failure is forgetting to put the hen back on the nest – the eggs become chilled.

To cover your options it's best to run two broodies at once, ideally in a double sitting box. This way you give yourself a bit of insurance in the event of problems. The other option is to split the hatching eggs between two birds to reduce the risk of desertion. Some breeders I know like to start the eggs on alternate days, so that the chicks hatch 24 hours apart. This means that the first chicks can be transferred to one broody as they hatch with the other hen hatching the second clutch. All these tricks help ensure a successful hatch.

The key thing is to allow nature to take its course, and not to get too excited and constantly check the hen. Remember, she has been left alone for three or four weeks and does not want or need repeated interruptions as the chicks are hatching.

Moving on

With the brood safely hatched, the broody and chicks should be moved to a proper broody coop and run.

Try and ensure that the eggs hatch over a weekend, when you're around to keep an eye on things. We used to keep the broody sitting boxes and coop on a stretch of grass by the vegetable garden. This was ideal for two reasons; it was away from the other birds, and the newly-hatched broods could be monitored during the important first few days as we would be working in the vegetable garden anyway.

The litter for the coop should be wood shavings (do not use straw at any time). The chicks will find straw difficult early on. Use a flat dish and feed proprietary chick crumb – the hen will call the chicks and teach them to eat. She will also scratch the feed around the coop. This is normal so don't worry about it. Give clean water in a small 'chick font' (available from most suppliers). This will allow a regular supply of water, but the chicks cannot drown. Incidentally, chick crumb and water will also be fine for the hen at this stage. If you want to feed a treat, then very finely-chopped egg and spring onion sprinkled on the crumbs will

be much enjoyed by the hen and her brood.

Keep the hen confined to the coop until the chicks are at least a week old. Allow the chicks access to a small run, but keep the hen inside to avoid chicks being run off their feet. After a week, the hen can have access to the run as well. By the time the chicks are three weeks old, they'll need to be moved to a larger run. Remember to shut the hen and her brood up every night to keep them safe and secure from predators such as foxes or cats.

The hen should stay with the chicks for at least 6-8 weeks (4-6 weeks for waterfowl). Then after this time simply remove her and return her to the other adults. Don't worry if, soon after hatching, the hen begins to moult. This is completely natural as the hen is starting to get ready to lay again.

Have a go!

Can you meet all these requirements? If so, then why not try having your eggs incubated naturally? There is so much pride and pleasure to be derived from

FINALLY...

During the research for this series I sat several broodies to provide pictures for the articles. Not all proved to be reliable sitters and this is a risk you take when sitting naturally. One of mine, after hatching 12 lovely ducklings and caring for them for a week, decided to start eating their feet, literally. We had to put down four, which was very sad. The remaining eight were given to another hen which had ducklings a week older. Fortunately, she adopted the new birds, gathered them up under her feathers and everything was fine from then on. Thank goodness hens cannot count! The offending broody was taken back to the laying house, and fitted with a big red leg ring to warn us of her unsuitability in the future.

So always remember that nature's way can be very rewarding, but it can also be very much 'in the raw with tooth and claw'.

simply watching a broody with her newly-hatched brood out in the spring sunshine. •

Chow down

Ensuring that your poultry are fed the right type of food at the right time is an important part of good husbandry, as Terry Beebe explains

There's a bit of a tendency among many keepers to take poultry feeding regimes for granted. The assumption is that filling the feeders and scattering a few treats on the ground is all there is to it. In reality, of course, there's a little more to the subject than that and, if your birds are to remain in tip-top condition, it's important to appreciate what's involved.

The first thing to understand is that birds have different dietary needs at various times of the year. Important times such as the breeding season, the moult, periods of growth, hot summer weather and cold winter nights can all present different feeding demands. Events such as the moult are stressful for all birds and the assistance provided by a well thought-out diet can make a significant difference in helping them through it.

Currently, most keepers favour the ad lib approach to feeding, where suitable formulated feed is constantly available. Gravity-fed feeders like this suit this option very well.

Thankfully, modern feed manufacturers appreciate the subtleties involved, and produce a good range of carefully formulated and nutritionally balanced products to suit all eventualities.

Chick crumb

This feed, also known as 'starter feed', has a high protein content of approximately 18% to meet the needs of the rapidly-growing birds. All poultry keepers who breed will start their birds on this.

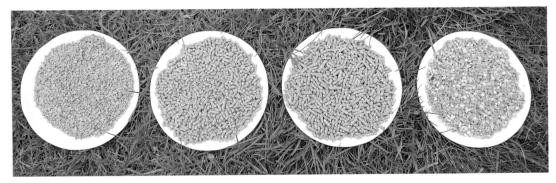
Feed options (from left to right); Chick crumb, grower/rearer pellets, layers pellets, mixed corn.

It's ideally suited to the task, being very finely milled so it's both easy to eat and digest.

As you would expect, chick crumbs are extremely nutritious, and can be fed from one-day-old onwards. It's recommended that young birds are kept on them for the first eight weeks, after which they can be gradually switched on to a growers' pellet that's designed to help specifically with the next stage of their natural development.

But chick crumb is also an ideal product to feed to adult birds during periods of stress (such as the moult). The high protein content acts as a great booster, and can also help with general recovery from illness.

Traditionally, chick crumb always contained an anti-coccidiosis treatment, but new manufacturing rules and regulations mean this is not necessarily the case now. You'll need to consult your supplier to be sure. There's an increasing demand these days for medication-free chick crumb, from keepers who want to protect their birds from these kinds of treatment. My personal view is a resounding thumbs-up for the medicated feed; I believe it's important to protect young birds from the terrible effects of the coccidiosis worm.

Grower/rearer feed

The protein content of this feed is slightly lower (15-16%) than that in chick crumb, and the vitamin and mineral content is carefully balanced to provide the ideal combination to carry birds right through to the point of lay (POL).

Having said this, if you've just bought-in a group of POL hens it's a good idea to keep them on a growers' feed for the first few weeks, allowing them to settle in to their new surroundings. Incidentally, the 'point of lay' can vary between 14 and 24 weeks old, depending on the breed.

I also use growers' feed for my show birds, when they are in moult – particularly the older ones. This seems to help to slow down the laying process, allowing them the maximum amount of time to feather-up and flourish.

Layers feed

Typically, most hens will come into lay at the 20-24 week mark, which is when they need to be switched on

Hanging the feeder inside the hen house is the neatest solution and provides more of a deterrent against rodents, although the birds won't enjoy the benefit of scratching around for a scattered feed.

Hens that are allowed the luxury of free-ranging will gain valuable exercise as they forage for natural food.

Chickens love treats but you must resist the temptation to feed them too much; it's for their own good!

to a specific layers formulation (16% protein). This provides a good, balanced diet that'll help the hens to perform well (maximum egg numbers, good shell quality, rich yolk), but the changeover should be made gradually, over a period of a week or so. Switching suddenly may cause a reluctance to feed. Chickens are very habitual creatures, and don't like sudden change.

Once your birds are established and laying well, then you may wish to give them a supplementary treat as well. My advice is to feed only a scatter of corn in the afternoon. It's very important not to overdo this, though; too much will quickly cause the birds to start favouring the corn to their layers ration, which is not good news. The weight will pile on and, as a consequence, ultimate egg production is likely to suffer.

Breeder feed

This option, as its name suggests, is formulated especially to increase the vigour in the breeding stock. It has a protein content of 18-19% and high levels of calcium, amino acids and vitamins. In addition, the manufacturers include a cocktail of various oils – soya, linseed and maize – to maximise fertility levels.

When rearing a flock, the birds you select to be your next breeders can be fed on this feed from POL up to and through the first breeding season. This applies to both male and female birds.

Natural feeding

If your birds enjoy a free-range lifestyle over a decent area they'll be able to collect most of the food they need during the day. This, combined with the exercise they get from doing it, should keep them fit and healthy. Of course, much depends on the area available. Running hens on fresh grass is just about ideal but, if the land is poor and has become 'stripped' from over-use, then the benefits available will be minimal.

However, in both cases, I believe there's still a need to give the birds constant access to a supply of professionally-formulated layers feed. All the main types of feed ration are available either as pellets or mash (meal), and the choice between the two is one of personal preference. Most keepers these

days prefer the convenience of pelleted feed, although some traditionalists stick with mash. The latter contains the same ingredients, but in a loose form – a bit like muesli. It can be ground to different degrees of coarsness, and fed either dry or wet (mixed with water to a crumbly consistency – warmed in the winter). Advocates claim that mash, which is slightly cheaper than pellets, is digested more effectively by their birds. But, on the downside, one disadvantage can be that the birds are able to feed selectively – eating only the parts they like best, and leaving the rest. Also, fed dry mash will produce dust which can have knock-on effects on health.

Split maize

This is an ideal feed supplement for improving yolk colour; it'll also enhance the yellow leg colour on birds that have it. It's particularly good to use in winter because it increases the birds' body temperature. Other benefits include the facts that it's a rich source of vitamin A, it's easy to digest and the birds love it.

Treats

The feeding of treats (wheat, vegetables, bread, kitchen scraps etc) is acceptable provided it's kept to a sensible level. There are a couple of good reasons for not over-feeding treats, and the first is that feeding bread and kitchen scraps will reduce or even stop hens laying.

Vegetables represent a good addition to the diet, especially spinach, chicory, Brussels sprouts and broccoli; all of which are rich in vitamins and very suitable for the birds.

Feeding wheat and corn needs also to be classed as a treat; a small handful scattered on to the pen floor helps keep the birds active and interested. But the moderation rule still applies. Too much and your birds will start running to fat, affecting their general health and laying performance.

The second important point to note is that the over-feeding of scraps and treats can lead to wastage which, in turn, will attract rats and mice. Avoid this at all costs. Don't leave feed and/or treats

FEEDING SUMMARY

1 day to 7-8 weeks old	Chick crumb
8-20 weeks old	Grower/Rearer
20 weeks onwards	Layers

Remember that a chicken's body is approximately 50% water so, as well as the appropriate feed ration, birds need constant access to a supply of fresh, clean drinking water.

accessible to rodents or wild birds. By keeping the area clean and tidy you'll minimise the risk of rodent infestation which, once established, can be an extremely difficult and expensive problem to deal with.

Feeding options

You have various choices when it comes to the way in which you deliver the food for your birds. You can scatter it directly on to the ground, use a trough/bowl or the hanging/free-standing units which can be filled to capacity and left to provide feed constantly until they are empty.

Scatter feeding does tend to help keep the birds occupied and exercised, which are both important considerations but, as I've already mentioned, leftovers can pose a problem. Containing the feed in a trough or bowl is slightly better in this respect, although the activity aspect is lost, obviously.

In my view, hanging feeders offer the safest, cleanest and most efficient way of delivering the food to your hens. These units are available in a range of sizes, but spillage can still remain a bit of a problem – chickens are simply messy eaters! The fact that hanging feeders are off the ground and typically lidded does reduce their attractiveness to rodents, but the risks remain.

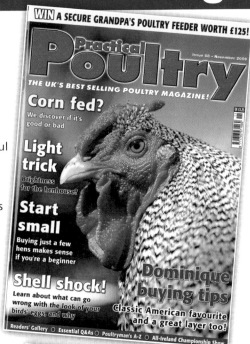

Invaluable records

Murray Guy explains the value of setting up a reliable records system, whether you own a garden flock of chickens or are committed to breeding pure-bred poultry

Maybe you are a small-scale hobbyist, simply enjoying your 'chooks' as they potter around the garden controlling those pesky slugs and snails as well as providing tasty, fresh eggs – or maybe you're a full-on enthusiast, breeding and showing pure-bred poultry. But whatever your experience level, the time needed to feed and maintain your birds seems increasingly difficult to find, as we all get busier with less and less free time... and those keepers who choose to breed and/or show their birds have an even tougher job as far as time management is concerned!

Establishing a straightforward record-keeping system can make the whole process of effective flock management a good deal simpler. While this may not sound like the most exciting topic for a chapter in this book, believe me, no matter how basic the system, keeping precise breeding, health and performance details about your birds can prove genuinely useful in all sorts of ways.

What to record?

Why bother keeping records at all? It's a question I'm often asked. Lots of people wonder what use they can possibly be, and even suggest that they haven't got the time to do it.

To answer to these reactions, I'd like to begin by summarising the sort of information that I now jot down concerning my birds. Hopefully this will illustrate to you the benefits to be gained.

Acquisition notes

You may have acquired your birds from a commercial egg-production unit, where the chicken's job was simply to push out egg after egg under torrid conditions. Alternatively, maybe you bought them from a breeder, or picked them up at a poultry auction. It can be of great benefit to know how old they were and where they originated from. Depending on how many birds you own, and how good your memory is, it maybe a challenge later on to remember every single detail on every bird you own! So simply jotting down some basic purchase information at the time is always a sensible move.

Recording information about which foster hens are capable of rearing other species – Runner ducks, in this case – can be very useful

These differently-sized birds were reared together. Only good records allow you to be certain about their actual ages

Identification

It goes without saying, but if you're going to keep records, you must first be able to identify your birds reliably. Colour and sex will usually be enough if you only keep a few birds. But dealing with larger numbers can become confusing.

Even if the birds are 'always' kept in the same pens, you never know when a mix-up may occur. Coloured plastic leg bands are probably your best way to identify individual specimens, and can also be very useful if birds are shy about coming too close. These rings are available in various types and colours, but if you find you're running out of colour combinations, then you can always start ringing the bird's other leg.

If you want to go 'large-scale', then numbered bands are probably the way to go. A word of warning though; bands can deteriorate and fade over time, so whenever you handle a bird, check the quality of its band, as it may need replacing.

Egg production

Wouldn't it be great to know for sure which hens are your best producers? Even though poultry keeping is probably only a hobby to you, it still may be useful to know which birds are the better producers – even if it's simply for the pleasure of knowing who lays the oversized eggs!

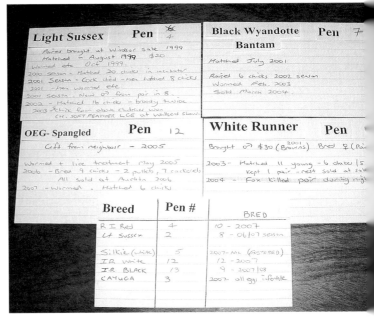

Examples of a simple record card system that can be updated when an incident arises, or at the end of a breeding season

Behaviour changes

I have observed my share of 'odd' poultry behaviour over the years, and I find it useful to note down which bird does what. This helps me build a better understanding of the overall goings-on within the flock.

Having recorded details like the odd seasonal occurrence, or possibly something that a bird may develop later in life, means that I have a potentially enlightening behavioural history to refer to should a problem develop that might be explained by earlier incidents.

Breeding notes

These are probably the most time-consuming to compile if you're a serious breeder. It may be important to gather and record all relevant information on pairings, breeding results and the parentage of birds in your flock (especially if genetics and line-breeding are of significance to your program).

Incubation notes

You may want to keep a daily log of your incubator's temperature, humidity and your egg-turning details (if it's not an 'auto'

machine). Records like this will enable you to back-track to where a problem might have been if a poor hatch occurs.

An additional comment section for details about when eggs start to pip internally/externally may provide important information if a chick is taking a particularly long time to hatch. The chick may

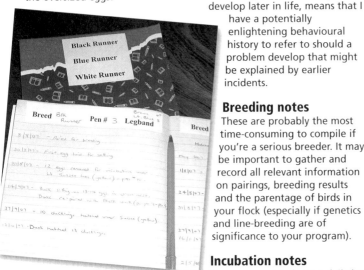

Information can be added to a notebook, with important details such as breed, sex and pen number. Record-keeping isn't rocket science!

Another way of keeping records is to write on the reverse of show cards, which is also helpful for identifying which bird was placed where, and at which show.

require some assistance from you, or you may want to know exactly how long it's been since hatching started.

Writing (in pencil) on the actual eggs when first laid and set – with details of the date, breed or pen/pair number – is also very valuable. This type of information is a good start to your breeding notes for pairs, and can be used to help highlight and explain problems with fertility and/or hatching.

Always remember, though, that disappointing hatching results can be the result of poor nutrition or a lack of vigour within the breeding stock; it's certainly not always the fault of the incubator!

Rearing information

A similar type of daily log to record such details as the brooder temperature, feeding time, amount consumed, growth weights of young, plus any general comments/observations.

Any of this information may be as elaborate as required. From time to time, school students requiring day-old ducklings for projects have contacted me. This type of rearing information would no doubt be useful in such instances.

Cross-fostering

There are a good number of reasons why you'd want to identify the best foster mothers among your hens. These include assessing their suitability for the hatching and rearing of the same species, or doing the same with other species. It's also useful to know whether a hen that won't hatch her own chicks will nevertheless take to and rear others. Sometimes, 'foster hens' require a special trick to encourage them to accept and foster young. Making a note of what this is can be useful too.

Then there's also the issue of whether they need to be incubating for a full incubation period prior to accepting young, plus the possibility of them being used to rear waterfowl or Game birds. Most importantly of all, do they do the job properly?

Medical

Keeping a record of when you last treated your birds for internal and external parasites, as well as noting

By using coloured, numbered leg bands you can increase your identification combinations. Note that fading colours or numbers should be replaced periodically to prevent possibly losing the identity of an individual

any particular medical problems that you witness, could prove important, especially if you find you have a health problem within your flock.

Making notes about which product was used, and how effective it was, can also be very useful in the future. Likewise, it's sensible to record birds that are vaccinated in your flock, whether

Plastic leg bands come in a variety of colours, types and sizes.

brought in or bred by yourself, and to make a note of when pen furniture was last treated for external parasites, such as mites.

Dispersal notes

For whatever reason, you may want to keep in touch with the person you sold birds to; in my experience, many a friendship has sprung from a chance poultry sale! On the down side, you may have struck a disaster within your flock, and might need to acquire progeny from your line of birds to restart your flock from a previous buyer.

General records

Headings such as 'breed', 'sex', 'age', 'colour', 'legband' and 'pen number' are probably just about all you need to establish a general record of the birds you're keeping.

Information can be written on a record card, in a notebook or kept on the home computer; a simple Word document or Excel spreadsheet can be used for each specimen, pair or pen. Then simply fill in the date and details of the occurrence. But remember to have a printed hard copy somewhere, as the last thing you want is to lose years of stored information to a computer gremlin.

Short cuts

If time isn't always on your side, you can write down a few 'quick notes' on a calendar or in a pocket notebook while you're in the garden or the hen house. Or, how about a blackboard or whiteboard in your feed shed?

One of the great attractions of poultry keeping is that there are so many different approaches – everyone has their favourite methods. This applies to record keeping as well. You can make it as simple or as complicated as you wish, depending on your circumstances, level of experience and requirements.

From a personal perspective, I've always found it interesting to go back over old entries to see what actually *did* happen rather than what my memory suggests happened. The mind can play funny tricks, so seeing it in front of you in black-and-white – especially in *your own* handwritting – means there can be no arguments! •

Man-made colour

Fred Hams explains how some of the most popular colours were created in our poultry pure breeds

BUFF ORPINGTONS

Reproduced by André & Sleigh, Limited. Bushey, Herts.

When, in 1894, Cook introduced the Buff variety of Orpington, he gave its parentage as being two parts Buff Cochin, one part Gold Spangled Hamburgh and one part Dark Dorking. This proved controversial on more than one count; the similar Lincolnshire Buff was already popular in the East of England, and there were many not ready for the concept of more than one variety within a breed. While the other varieties of Orpington soon assumed the same type and degree of fluff that rapidly became associated with the Black, the Buff retained feathering compatible with a more utility role for nearly 100 years. This illustration by Ludlow (1900) shows a type prevalent until the introduction of continental strains in the 1990s.

Crossing existing breeds, and selectively breeding from the offspring to create brand new breeds, is largely a late-19th century concept. Looking at each of those breeds in depth would require another book, but here it's worth emphasising some points about the relationship between bred-in colour varieties and standardised breeds.

In the days before the advent of organised shows, it would seem likely that some poultry breeders had either selected strains contained within local fowl populations to enhance certain colours and colour patterns or, while selecting for traits like the

ability to fight, strain identity often became synonymous with a single colour or pattern.

Sebright exception

The one exception to this is the Sebright bantam, created by one man seeking what he considered to be perfection at the beginning of the 19th century, 50 years before the first proper poultry show. However, this was a breeding concept that would be repeated with some fascinating parallels when, in the 1870s, the Americans created the Wyandotte.

It was probably wider conflicts with the concept of creation that led the early pre-Darwin poultry authors to treat poultry that arrived from Asia as specific breeds, believing that they had existed since the dawn of time in the regions around the ports where they were said to have come from, rather than being representatives of the poultry populations of those regions. The fact that the offspring from the crossing of two of these populations (from very different parts of Asia) were quickly accepted as a 'pure breed', owed much to the breeders anointing them with the title 'Brahma'.

With its tweaked hybrid vigor, the Brahma probably influenced utility development more than any of the other soft-feather imports. Certainly, most of the varieties of Sussex that were developed during the second half of the century owed much of their genetic make-up to the two original Brahma varieties, both of which – being genetically silver – endowed the Light Sussex with the ability to produce, when crossed with a gold male, sex-linked chicks.

During the same period that the Sussex breeders were adding any genetic element that they thought likely to improve the table qualities of their local breed (c1860-1900), the American were busy creating the Rhode Island Red. With no indigenous poultry breeds, but a rich supply of European breeds and Asiatic strains arriving at the Atlantic ports, breeders in America's maritime states enjoyed an unrivaled advantage when it came to producing the world's most successful heavy-breed layer.

PARTRIDGE COCHINS

It's unlikely that the Asiatic form of partridge marking introduced with the Cochin-type fowl in the 1850s would have been as distinct as shown in this Ludlow illustration of 1902.

That these early breeders' initial choice was a workaday brown (genetically gold, though later 'Red') enabled crosses between it and the Light Sussex to dominate commercial poultry production throughout most of the next century. Both the Rhodes and Sussex were, rather than being 'purpose-bred', gradually selected to fulfill a utility purpose.

Purpose-made

The concept of the 'purpose-made' breed – looking at existing breeds and deciding which and in what proportions to add to the mixture of other breeds, to obtain a given result – is a very different one. Good examples include the Wyandotte, Plymouth Rock and the British Orpington. While we only accepted Hamburghs as worthy of notice (probably because they fitted the mould of our northern group of breeds), the pattern of immigration into the United States would have been accompanied by their largely barred local breeds and populations. Inter-breeding between these is the likely source of the Dominique, that could have played an all-important role in the creation of the Barred Plymouth Rock.

But a whole range of early pedigrees detailing the probable descent of the first (and barred) Rocks has been published, recording at least four prototypes. But what has to be questioned is the second cross between a single-combed Dominique-coloured male and a Black Java which, if we're to believe the often-published pedigree *(Fig. A)*, seems to have been left out of the final mix. As the Black Java appears to belong firmly within the Langshan/Shanghai group of breeds, it seems wholly likely that the published pedigrees were drawn-up retrospectively and that, like many of our European cuckoo and barred breeds, the Barred Rocks plumage pattern owes much to the inter-breeding between the new pattern of penciling introduced from Asia,

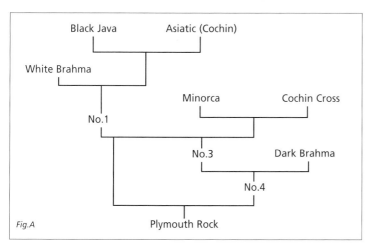

Fig.A

and older, fine barring found in many of the northern European populations. Looking at the material available, it seems probable that the Dominique did play a formative role in the creation of the barred variety and, when we see how narrow this baring can become with selection, it's not difficult see parallels with breeds like the Campine; another ancient fowl of northern Europe and Turkey.

Another aspect to the 'concept breeds' is that once a breed has been established in one colour, or even before it's fully established, other colour varieties that conform to the overall breed type but which may have very different parentage could be 'made' in other way to the original variety. In the case of the Buff Rock, while it has probably been remade more than once, the original formula is reported as being Light Brahma on a cross between Buff Leghorn and a Buff Cochin.

Had the end result not been very different to the original concept (3), the Wyandotte could perhaps have provided a better example of the purpose-bred breed. It seems likely that the original intention, when a Sebright bantam was crossed with a Cochin hen, was to produce an improved Cochin bantam. However, when their size proved to be rather large, they were offered as 'Sebright Cochins'. Other crosses including that of Silver Hamburgh and a Dark Brahma, seem to have helped stabilise the comb as rose, rather than pea. But even to this day, particularly when breeders select for really good rose combs, the amount of Cochin in the overall Wyandotte make-up probably results in them having to expect a number of single-combed sports. The Gold-laced Wyandotte seems to have resulted from an infusion of (probably rose-combed) Rhode Island Red and, via a far more complex route, further infusions of Buff Cochin – the Buff Wyandotte *(Fig. B)*.

Multi-coloured breeds

By the time further multiple crosses between Golden Wyandottes, Partridge Cochins, and Gold-penciled Hamburghs had produced

The White Orpington rarely carried as much feather and fluff as the Black variety. This group of pullets, bred by Fred Hams and being shown to Will Burdett, would have laid as well as the Buffs of the same, early 1980s period.

the Partridge variety, the concept of a breed made up of many varieties had been established. If type defines breed, the Wyandotte would have inherited much of its round, curving outline, and some of its feather shape, from the Brahma and Cochin; its rose comb with its single leader from the Hamburgh and its yellow legs and shin colour from every one of its ancestors other than the Sebright (way back in the original mix).

When we look at the feather coloration and, more importantly, the colour patterns involved and find all the elements that man had been seeking to define and refine in the years before c1860, those later standardised Wyandotte patterns can strike a fresh resonance. Of the earlier pattern, both the lacing from the Sebright and the Hamburgh's spangling that played a part in its own ancestry, were capable of contributing to new feather patterns when combined with those introduced with the heavy-boned Asiatics imported during the 1850s.

Here the most important

pattern factor was a new form of penciling that consisted of concentric rings of a darker colour on a lighter ground-colour, as in the female (silver) Dark Brahma and the (gold) Partridge Cochin. Left unchecked in self-coloured varieties, the excessive fluff that also came with these Asiatics could swamp both type and utility potential but, when selected to conform to precise patterns, failed to compromise Wyandotte type.

For many, the flagship Wyandotte is the original, laced variety; a rounded, largely fluff-free feather is the ideal shape to demonstrate both perfect lacing and a true Wyandotte type (essentially, controlled curves). The lacing can be shown to be both slightly different to – and even an improvement on – that found on the Sebright. When Punnett (1923) crossed a Silver Sebright with a Golden Spangled Hamburgh, out of 299 offspring only 44 were laced and only four were comparable with the Sebright. But, when Agar (1924) back-crossed the female offspring from Barred Rock male on Golden Wyandotte to a Gold-laced Wyandotte, he produced both gold and silver offspring all indistinguishable from pure Wyandottes of those patterns.

There's always likely to some conflict between intricate colour patterns and breed type. Recently we've seen criticism of the barring on winning barred Wyandottes, by those who've failed to realise that the perfectly straight barring seen on the Plymouth Rock has been seen (at least in this country) by selecting some exhibition examples of the latter breed for excessively narrow feathering.

Golden Wyandotte	Creamy-white Wyandotte		Golden Wyandotte	Creamy-white Wyandotte

Fig.B diagram:

Golden Wyandotte + Creamy-white Wyandotte → Buff Cochin

Golden Wyandotte + Creamy-white Wyandotte → Golden Wyandotte

Buff Cochin + Golden Wyandotte

Golden Wyandotte + Buff Cochin

→ Buff Wyandotte

Cochin, one part Gold Spangled Hamburgh and one part Dark Dorking. This introduction was to prove controversial on more than one count; partly because the similar Lincolnshire Buff was already popular in the East of England, and there were many fanciers not yet ready for the concept of more than one variety within a breed. For all the next century the Buffs, which had a separate club, remained sufficiently less fluffy to fill the domestic role that Cook originally intended for his Blacks, if not the utility role. Jubilee Orpingtons – really tri-coloured spangles – appeared in 1897, in time for Queen Victoria. But, to confuse matters, black and white mottles arrived in 1900 and were labeled 'Spangled'.

The complex and precise nature meant that those who liked the jubilee pattern found it easier to perfect as Speckled Sussex, and the Mottles dropped by the wayside for most of the next century. Whites made in 1893-8 were said to include a range of breeds but, eventually, absorbed so many white sports from Blacks and Buffs that they finally assumed a feather structure and type very like the former. Breeders of Blues that derived from crosses between Blacks and Whites, soon found that they could be selected to have the same feather structure as the Blacks; that is, so long as they were not expected to have crisp lacing that the early standard asked for. Summarily, those breeding the recently introduced laced varieties are likely to encounter similar conflict between colour and type.

Feather shape is always likely to either enhance or inhibit feather pattern. Barred Plymouth Rocks have, over the years, been selected at least in this country with very narrow feathers because this facilitates very fine and straight barring. Barred Wyandottes can be selected that have the same round feathering and body shape as the laced varieties but barring on a wide feather won't be as straight as that on a narrow one. As we are now seeing, more and more colours and varieties transfer between breeds. Breeders, judges and those charged with regulatring standards may have to re-think old concepts. •

Apart from showing just how quickly golden feathers can fade even in Spring sunlight, this photograph of a Gold-laced Orpington illustrates the conflict between breeding for a precise feather pattern, and the degree of feather and fluff that has become an accepted part of the breed type.

Utility range

When William Cook set out to combine the best qualities of several breeds, he had as a concept a range of utility fowl, each suitable for varying domestic and commercial situations. He'd earlier been an advocate of crosses between very different breeds – like Black Minorca x Black Plymouth Rock – and, at that stage, genetic distance would have been more noticeable than that available to late hybridists. From there it was a short step to using another sire on this (and possibly other crosses), and then to inter-breed the offspring to a point where subsequent generations could be said to 'breed true'.

The all-important third element in the early crosses was the clean-legged Langshan that serious breeders were parting with because they failed to meet the standard for the new breed – Cook insisting that they laid better than those with the required feathered legs. When introduced in 1886 the original black variety was marketed as being suitable for residents of towns and industrial districts. Exhibitors, with an eye to the show bench, seem to have both introduced the by-then very fluffy Black Cochin, and selected profusely feathered fowl.

When, in 1894, Cook introduced the buff variety, he gave its parentage as being two parts Buff

Breeding from hybrids

Fred Hams looks into the viability of producing worthwhile utility fowl from a hybrid-based breeding program

A typical hybrid pullet from one of today's most successful lines, sired by a very utility Rhode Island Red.

Nowadays, the possibility of creating 'designer' breeds and strains is often a topic of discussion. So I think it's worth considering exactly what's on offer at the moment, and the ways in which the current genetic material can best be used. First, though, it's important to remember that this is a branch of poultry breeding that's been largely sidelined by academia, and abandoned by the industry, for more than 40 years.

Like many others, my own experience of utility poultry breeding is of being on the edge of an industry that continued to distance itself from me, rather than me from it. And, like most earlier breeders, much of my assessment is based on informed guesswork, and is tinged with a philosophical approach to how we view domestic utility.

Available genetic resources may well be found to split roughly into four categories; the old, standard-bred breeds whose ancestors were the basis of the pre-hybrid laying flock; breeds of pure breeds that, while playing little part in yesterday's poultry industry, are either inherently good layers of albeit rather small eggs, or have other useful qualities; those strains of bantam that have retained more of their utility qualities than most of their large counterparts; the pick of the hybrid laying strains that now dominate both the industrial flocks and much of the domestic market as well.

To better understand the potential role of either the old utility strains or their later, hybrid counterparts, it'll be useful to take a brief look at the development of the former to the point that they and they alone provided the basis and platform for the creation of the latter.

Careful selection

Selection on the basis of either laying trials or individual home (trap-nest) recording that began in earnest just after the First World War, saw egg numbers increase in the most highly-developed strains by up to 50% by the start of the Second World war. While this overall increase was shared by eight or 10 heavy breeds, two or three varieties have consistently

Photograph]   [G. S. McCann, Uttoxeter

FIG. 4.– Male Progeny of Father and Daughter INBRED and Control Matings
Progeny of the Control matings are indicated with an asterisk.

Photograph]   [G. S. McCann, Uttoxeter

FIG. 5.– Female Progeny of Father and Daughter INBRED and Control Matings
Progeny of the Control matings are indicated with an asterisk.

When individual birds were found to perform better in laying trials and egg recording programs, breeders tried to establish this trait by 'in-breeding' within close family groups. While some sibling groups often laid better than their less inbred cousins, many thought that inbreeding would nevertheless lead to both lack of size and stamina.

But males from the same brown egg-laying breeds were expected to provide much of the poultry meat, and this lack of size could be seen as important. So the Ministry of Agriculture started a series of experiments in 1924-5 and, by 1934, it was possible to demonstrate that successive inbred generations lost size. However, it was soon found that crosses between unrelated strains of inbred birds restored both size and vigour.

Today, most of our very few utility pure-bred strains have, out of necessity, been subjected to a degree of inbreeding. As industrial poultry selection continued, it was found that techniques like progeny testing could reduce bird size without affecting egg weight or numbers. The two examples above each show White Wyandottes that have a similar overall type to Marianne Oliver's White Sussex that are, themselves, products of controlled inbreeding.

provided individual hens that laid over 275 eggs a year (close to a hybrid's total).

The usual method used to establish this trait within a family was to head breeding pens with males bred from related, highest-performing hens, which led to many of these extended families (strains) becoming quite inbred. One

method of trying to combat any perceived resulting weakness, and to preserve the dual-purpose or table properties of some strains, was to save the largest available males. Soon it was found that inbreeding within one strain could provide extra (hybrid) vigour when crossed with another inbred strain of either the same or another breed.

The years on either side of the Second World War saw many hatchery-based breeders use the technique of merging two inbred lines to produce the female half of the breeding pen, mated to an even more inbred male line that produced a final (terminal) generation with optimum (hybrid) vigour. Economy of scale enabled the later, often internationally-based, breeding companies to use similar, if refined, programs to make and effectively market their hybrids.

The first things to appreciate about these hybrids are that they are neither 'hybrids', and nor are the generations we buy 'terminal'. One early innovation used by larger breeding companies was progeny-tested male lines that broke the old reliance on female-only line recording. This, in turn, completely changed the old perception that, all other things being equal, the biggest available male had to be the best. In fact, time and again, the smaller males proved to produce female offspring that laid both more and larger eggs than their larger siblings.

Big business

Taking this sort of breeding program though all its permutations took more resources than had ever been available to the earlier poultry industry. With much of the investment in the first hybrids coming from companies that made fortunes out of hybrid corn (maize) strains that were true hybrids, there was an early perception that, unlike their forebears, the old first crosses could not be bred-on from. This, in turn, enabled their creators to franchise their new products to large sections of the industry.

The fact that these hybrids were smaller than their forebears – the old first crosses – was welcomed by an industry in which egg production had moved to battery cages, and poultry meat production was relying on very specialised table strains. Much of this development was made on the basis of an affluent consumers' preference for large eggs.

Another downside of 40 year's laying fowl selection is that a few parent lines are now owned by some of the world's largest

The White Leghorn-based hybrids may be the world's most successful fowl bred on hybrid lines, but can be found to contain so little genetic diversity that they are themselves ripe for an outcross. Given the right sire, the possibilities are both exciting and wide. The outcome itself could be seen as hybrid.

companies and generally aren't available; the even more select grandparent lines tend to be kept far removed from end users too.

Now that keeping a few hens needs to make more financial sense to an increasing number of small-scale poultry keepers, many could find themselves questioning the viability of continuing to buy expensive replacement pullets. This then raises the question: 'Could we breed our own?' Encouragingly, the answer could be 'yes', but not before an awful lot of homework.

For a start those interested in this option have to face the fact that, at best, there is only a handful

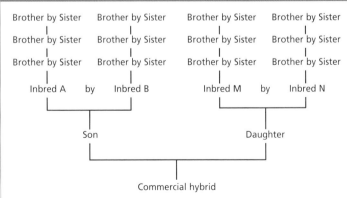

INBREEDING, AND COMBINING INBRED LINES, FOR THE PRODUCTION OF COMMERCIAL HYBRID POULTRY

Brother by Sister   Brother by Sister   Brother by Sister   Brother by Sister

Brother by Sister   Brother by Sister   Brother by Sister   Brother by Sister

Brother by Sister   Brother by Sister   Brother by Sister   Brother by Sister

Inbred A   by   Inbred B   Inbred M   by   Inbred N

Son   Daughter

Commercial hybrid

The type of program used to produce the early hybrid laying strains. Many later programs used similar methods to produce the female parent lines, and another unrelated and often different breed or colour line for the male parent element. What this diagram does not show, unfortunately, is the methods used in the selection of these lines.

Not everyone is looking to produce the ultimate layer – some want to end up with a good layer that has a reasonable carcass. Geoff Silcock's table strain of New Hampshire Red that won the Practical Poultry Utility Cup at the 2009 Royal Show could be capable, when used on typical brown egg-laying hybrid hens, of producing a generation of females that lay reasonably well and males that are traditionally-shaped.

BIG EATERS?

Jo, a research ecologist, has made some interesting observations with her own bantams and has reached the following conclusion.

"It's often pointed out that, relative to their body weight, bantams need to eat more than large fowl to maintain body temperature, thereby making them less useful as utility birds. The physics are undeniable; the surface area to volume ratios are far higher in small objects, so more heat is radiated.

"Our bantams, though just a quarter the weight of large fowl, nevertheless lay an egg about two thirds the size of the large fowl egg. Doing the sums, the bantam egg is 2.7 times larger than you would expect *pro rata*. Our bantams plainly don't eat 2.7 times the food consumed by large fowl. In other words, the effect of surface area/volume ratio is more than compensated for by egg size.

"The only conclusion can be that bantams possess some innate advantage over large fowl in their egg production. In particular, conversion efficiency (egg weight as a proportion of food consumed) has to be much higher."

of strains of the old, pre-hybrid, heavy breed layers that are in any way comparable with today's hybrids. So it could be that, like those who've found that to produce the ultimate weight of eggs for a given amount of food, we have to start thinking 'outside the box', and look at the poultry world's greatest genetic source; the mainline hybrid laying flock.

You may think that, in looking more closely at this idea, it surely wouldn't be difficult to come up with a list of what we'd get if keepers decided to cross 'this' hybrid with 'that' hybrid. Sadly, this isn't possible. The best we can offer, based on years spent on the fringes of the breeding industry, are a few guidelines as to what could 'nick' (an old term often used to cover intuitive breeding decisions) with what.

For example, having watched a breeding company use the American New Hampshire Reds that were part of a franchise on their Rhode X Sussex, Geoffrey Marston used some of their spare cockerels on his White Sussex to produce crosses that laid well over 280 eggs, which was certainly competitive with the then-hybrids. The fact that

nearly all of today's popular brown egg-laying hybrids have at least 50% Rhode in them (far more if one includes the 'white' and 'silver' Rhodes that have replaced the old Light Sussex as dams of all of the brown-feathered examples) could put a new value on the remnants of yesterday's strains.

As in all utility breeding, it's the strains that are far more important than the breeds; inbred strains may have the ability to produce greater vigour in their out-crossed offspring. Here we can find the perfect example in John Leach's Rhodes, that directly descend as a 'closed flock' from a 1950s premier, gold medal strain. Spare males could be used on any of the black-feathered examples that have Plymouth Rock in their make-up – the successful brown egg laying hybrids – to produce at least one generation of worthwhile pullets. Pullets yes, but not sex-linked, so no feather determination, and further generations could be a whole new learning experience; as could back-crosses to some of our rather inbred bantam strains that could produce generations of small birds that lay relatively large eggs.

Hybrid challenge

Those hybrids, often marketed for some reason here as White Star, that derive so exclusively from White Leghorn that on a worldwide basis have no more genetic diversity than aunts and nieces, offer enormous challenges. Many years ago I was contacted by a lady who'd bred more than one generation by an exhibition white bantam cockerel, and wanted an outcross. Ian Sissons let me have a small black male and the subsequent generation, all white, laid lots of large eggs and, when mated brother-to-sister, split 75% white, 25% black that were used to make separate strains that can still be back-crossed resulting in little birds that lay up to 300 eggs in a year.

So it's perfectly possible to breed on, often with spectacularly good results, from those hybrid strains that we often overlook as terminal generations. On the other hand, as this is not a definite formula situation, there are likely to be nearly as many disappointments as successes. •

Not short on colour!

Fred Hams investigates the expansive range of Scots Dumpy colours and reveals his own breeding programme

There are few subjects more likely to confuse and occasionally divide breeders and 'fanciers' – and even judges and administrators – than the relationship between breed, variety and colour. It is over-simplistic to suggest that 'type defines the breed and colour the variety.'

Things can be complicated by the fact that, while colour in some breeds is considered extremely important, in others it's type that dominates, as illustrated by a disproportionate allocation of exhibition points. The latter point is often reinforced with reference to the old adage; 'there's no such thing as bad colour in a good Game cock'. This is a sentiment that dates from an earlier era when the birds used in cock-fighting mirrored the naturally occurring patterns of the countryside, and which can still be seen in the Oxford-based colours in large Old English Game. Arguably,

Starting with a mixed group of colours from a closed flock of Dumpy-type bantams and after further selection on the basis of Dumpy type, one of the first colour themes to emerge was the light and dark silver patterns as seen in early Dorking illustrations – another line developed from the rudimentary gold Columbian restriction as used by the late Victorian breeders to create breeds like the their Lincolnshire Buffs. These, along with a black line and some old type Game 'reds', are the sole ancestors of the pens now being used in the attempt to breed to both type and standard colours.

though, this has very little validity when applied to the exhibition-derived Game bantams.

Original colours

Our perception of the importance of colours and varieties within a breed structure will always have an historical basis until, perhaps, we moved to the more continental, *laissez faire* approach in some breeds that allows any standard colour to be shown.

Those breeds that had existed for hundreds of years before the 19th century importations of heavy-boned Asiatic fowl tended to be confined to those earlier, 'natural Game' colours, plus those pencilled, spangle and rudimentary laced patterns common to Northern Europe and Asia Minor.

Here, two points are worth noting. First the obvious correlation between gold and silver pencilled Hamburghs and ginger and perhaps, to a lesser extent, mealy-breasted greys, in the true Game fowl of old England. Secondly, nearly all of these ancient breeds are either poorly represented in bantam versions or, where the bantams are plentiful, the large versions tend to struggle to attain much greater size than their often relatively oversized miniature versions.

If we seek, as we often do, to show that the Scots Dumpy is a very ancient 'breed', we may have to challenge both our notion of breed and the definition of 'bantam'. When Scots Dumpies were first admitted to the standards in 1912 (though having been recorded intermittently since the first poultry shows some 60 years before), the standard required an overall shape

in line with the skeletal remains recorded in archaeological remains dating back up to 2,000 years. Ancient certainly, but a breed? The widespread distribution of shortened leg bones in archaeological remains suggests the existence of classically Dumpy-shaped fowl since earliest domestication.

Bantam or not?

The fact that nearly all the Roman bucolic authors refer to the existence of 'dwarf' or 'nanas' breeds, and that these appear as 'bantam' in most of the early English translations, could be explained by the coincidence that most were translated at the time when the first tiny fowl arrival in Europe from Java.

With a few notable exceptions, nearly all of the bones found at Roman (and later) sites are far smaller than those of modern poultry breeds. Finds of shorter-legged adults and some evidence of whole populations demonstrating the characteristic percentage of shortened leg bones begs the question: were many of these Roman dwarf fowl actually what

we would now call Dumpies or Creepers? Whether these would have been the white-lobed Creepers standardised in many countries, or the red-faced variety standardised here as Scots Dumpies is, of course, open to debate; as is the question of the colours they could have existed in.

As one of the best-documented records of a British population of dwarf, dumpy or creeper fowl comes from the bones found during an archaeological excavation of Viking settlement in York, it would seem wholly likely that these early 'Dumpies' would have either followed the gold and silver patterns of the Hamburgh-type Norse fowl, or the age-old, natural colour variations of our Game fowl. In this context, it's interesting to note that the very earliest coloured illustration of the breed seems to be a woodcut used (some years before either poultry shows or written standards) to illustrate a *c*1844 Bonington Moubray *Domestic Poultry*. In this the artist depicted the birds as being the same bright red as today's pencilled Hamburghs or ginger Game cocks.

New colours

This breed wasn't standardised for another 60 years, after the period that saw the importation of Asiatic fowl and which completely changed both the selection, and even the concept, of standard-bred fowl in the western world. This movement, that saw not only heavier-boned fowl but the establishment of colour varieties previously unknown in Europe (including the cuckoo pattern), is generally

The females in this breeding pen have faded in the sun but at point-of-lay were, like the male, the same colour pattern as that chosen by early, utility-minded Lincolnshire Buff breeders. Apart from being some of the easiest to breed to type, these are proving to be some of the best layers of surprisingly large eggs.

The early mix of colour patterns means that some interesting colours continue to turn up. Many of these will interest those whose enthusiasm is confined to the fascinating type and character of the breed and can, if shown, find a hope in the limited number of shows that put on classes for non-standardised colours where, however good their type, they are unlikely to be considered for further honours. The tri-colour (left) came from a mating made in an effort to reproduce the earlier mottled, the silver coming from a pen headed by a Dark Dorking-marked male. The latter pullet and sisters, though pretty enough, will be retained in an effort to breed silver pencilled offspring.

thought to be the result of the use of the 'new' strains with the ancient grey or silver pencilled varieties of northern Europe.

As these resulting breeds and varieties seem to have been ideally suited to conditions in much of northern Europe, it's little wonder that the pattern was favoured by Scottish breeders by the time the Dumpy was standardised. Evidence that there were still other than greys (cuckoos) exists in JW Brown's (the Scots Dumpy Club's then secretary) entry in *Feathered World's 1925 yearbook*: 'I notice the older breeders appear to watch type closely, not subjecting same to mere colour points, and consequently some real waddlers are found in the rare colours. These lesser-known colours are quite attractive, particularly the black and whites (something like the old Spangled Orpingtons), and the 'gamey' colourings. A few of these exhibited more often could help bring in more members.'

These comments, together with a reference in the same year to a Mr Paxton winning the AOV Cup at Paisley with a 'Dorking'-coloured hen, could be of great interest to the growing band trying to breed good type dumpy bantams in a variety of definable colours.

Even in those breeds, where the importance of type over colour is reinforced by a disproportionate number of points for the former, in the case of Dumpies the 10% of points awarded for colour have to be relevant to an attempt to breed and exhibit to any recognised colour standard. There is, or should be, a general understanding that with any exhibit of even those breeds where type is thought to be of utmost importance, judges have a standard against which they can award a percentage of points for colour.

Colour issues

The importance of this point when judges are adjudicating between breeds isn't always appreciated by exhibitors of euphemistically styled 'off-colour' OEG bantams. This has caused more than a few disputes, when higher show awards have been decided, and is unlikely to prove the 'get out' clause for colour in the new Serama bantam standard.

The fact that the bantam versions that are now being shown in both the old Game and early European colour patterns – and those emanating from the golden – are of Victorian standardization probably owes much to the population of Dumpy-type bantams that were passed on to me by the owner of the country's top Suffolk

Punch heavy horse studs. This dumpy gene that had become a dominant feature among a closed flock of otherwise typical farm bantams had been further encouraged by the simple process of culling all the long-legged males.

The resulting population – possibly due to linked genes – conformed remarkably closely to our standardised Dumpy type. As, through a set of circumstances, the flock was down to one, short-legged male, their owner more or less insisted that I took this male and the pick of the females and did something with them. As the descendants of this group went on to become the basis of those now being seen in increasing numbers at regional shows, the rest of this article is largely confined to a progress report on this lineage.

The one available little male was both small and of good type; black-bottled with white, similar to that seen in some of today's better Houdans. The rest of the flock would have probably represented a similar pool of colour patterns found in a typical Victorian farmyard. While all would have been of a similar genetic make-up, I confined my female selection to some of the shorter-legged birds.

Limited breeding

Then, after reassessing these, I continued by limiting the female element of the breeding pen to two more-or-less silver Columbians, two cinnamon buffs as seen on early Cochin prints, a rather heavily-marked Birchen and a black pullet that I rather hoped would at least moult-out mottled. With just the one male, an obvious first move was to build on what was already a pretty stable strain, and breed and select for true Dumpy type and stature. In the event, what turned up were varying birchens, brown reds, black-tailed buffs and whites, but no mottleds and only a few 'less than black, blacks'.

Given the vagaries and permutations of Dumpy breeding, this first crop contained a rather better than expected percentage of 'shorties'. After a couple of generations of breeding, what looked like similar colours and patterns together produced useable buff Columbians, buffs (as in Lincolnshire Buffs) and whites with black tails that are probably the silver counterpart of their gold Lincolnshire Buff-coloured cousins.

As breeding from pens of blacks continued to produce at least 50% females with either some gold or brown in their neck feathers, I accepted the offer of an undersized male out of one of the better strains of large Dumpies. As the later generations from this line are smaller than most of the other strains, this line has found its way into most of the later breeding pens.

While, with selection, each generation selected to conform to a specific colour pattern produces a percentage of better examples than its predecessors, there remains the 'sod's law' phenomenon of the odd throw-back to completely unexpected feather patterns. That many of these patterns hark back to an era when many of the foundation patterns were first selected by early breeders is fascinating, but not that surprising when one remembers that I first noticed this happening when carrying out a program of back-crossing between generations of White X Light Sussex.

The right type

Refining these colours will always be influenced by the necessity to select for type, and there will be those who contribute to the breed cause by being content to confine their efforts to breeding typey Dumpies.

However, with an increasing number of show schedules reflecting the Poultry Club's rules that allow Dumpies to be shown in any colour standardised in any other breed, those birds shown will have at least to present judges with the opportunity of awarding a percentage of the modest 10 colour points.

So far we've been lucky with our judges who've done what judges should do; read the standard and made judgements related to colour and type. Exhibitors of non-standard colours have had to accept that their birds would not be part of any further line-up. Perhaps predictably, it was a black that recently went forward to be Reserve Champion at the Surrey County Regional Championship Show.

That said, her line plays some part in most of the breeding pens currently being used to establish other colour patterns, and might auger well for the 'variety' Dumpy bantams, and those new members that the club secretary looked forward to back in 1926.

As we begin to distil the colours contained within the original Dumpy bantam population, a recurring theme seems to be the Game-coloured Reds that are now more often encountered among Oxford Game. It seems likely that time alone will demonstrate the exact female counterpart of the various shades of red males. This would also be that most natural of colour patterns, chosen by the early, utility-minded New Hampshire Red breeders as having the least likely impact on type.

Good enough to eat?

Andy Marshall says that the real bonus of producing your own poultry for the pot is that you know exactly what you're eating. But what does successful rearing-for-the-pot involve?

I've not bought chicken in a supermarket since I was an impoverished student in the 1970s. It's interesting to note that my son, Alasdair, who's now at university, not only stocks up with all the usual goodies from home, but raids the freezer for ample supplies of home-produced chicken and beef. When I asked him why recently, his reply was simple: "It cooks and tastes the best!"

If you want the satisfaction of eating a meal of home-produced meat and vegetables, don't expect to achieve it without some hard work, careful thought and plenty of forward planning.

Which birds?

The purchase of day-old chicks from a fattening strain is in some ways the easiest way to go but, in other respects, it's the hardest. What you must ask yourself is whether you're prepared to kill, pluck and dress 36 birds all at the same time? Do you have space in the freezer for that many? These are issues you must address prior to purchase of your day-old chicks because you won't

be able to buy these birds in ones or twos.

You're also very unlikely to be able to locate a supplier of potential fattening birds that will sell you growers. This business tends to work on big numbers, so things aren't set up for the DIY home producer. Even suppliers prepared to offer chicks in manageable numbers – less than 100 per order – are few and far between. Remember the hatcheries hatch in tens of thousands of day-olds, so these operations won't be prepared for the hassle of organising individual orders of just a few chicks for the domestic keeper.

Fortunately, though, there are suppliers of smaller batches. Check when ordering if the supplier does the hatching, or if it is simply selling-on chicks from another supplier. This is and important aspect as one of the fundamental principles of fattening is to get the chicks settled at the earliest age possible, so that they can then start to grow at their own speed.

Commercial table fowl are fattened in well under ten weeks.

they reach ten weeks old, at which point the fattening process can begin. The size and shape of the fattened birds depends on the breed. For example, a Sussex carries a massive amount of white breast meat, whereas a Spanish or Minorca produces far less meat, and it'll be darker too. You also have the option of allowing some of the males to grow into 'roasters', and others to be used purely as suppliers of breast and leg meat, plus livers.

The breast is used for a range of dishes including casseroles, pasta toppings or sandwiches. The legs and thighs make excellent curries or slowly-cooked stews with lentils. The livers are used for paté to be spread on crostini – ideal for a tasty, light lunch!

It's essential to remember that any birds for human consumption must not have been fed any medicated feed. The withdrawal period varies according to the feed company, so check your feed labels and speak to your supplier.

You can eliminate that problem by putting the fattening males on

Breeds such as the Sussex have traditionally been reared as meat birds, and males like this Buff will produce plenty of meat.

However, for those of us in the domestic environment, working to this sort of timescale simply isn't advisable as it's hard to achieve efficiently without the correct management. The danger of getting it wrong is that you'll introduce growth checks, which can result in the chick's digestive system being upset which, in turn, adversely affects the end result.

If, on the other hand, you are looking to fatten surplus males from your breeding program, then you need to adopt a slightly different *modus operandi*. The first thing to remember is that the birds will come through at different times, dependant on the frequency and size of hatches.

More meat

Providing you have adequate housing, the spare males can be separated from the females once

The Minorca produces tasty meat, although not in the same quantities as the Sussex.

layers feed, wheat and maize. Normally these three feed types aren't fed at the same time, but according to the results you're after. For example, young birds being fattened for breast and thigh meat are normally fed a diet of just proprietary layers mash with a grain feed in the evening (usually whole wheat). However, those being kept for roasting are put on to a whole-wheat diet with a maize top-up, three to four weeks before they are killed. This gives the bird a great bloom, plus an even layer of fat under the skin, which is important for a roasting bird.

It's also important to remember that home-produced birds look and taste different to the processed, mass-produced product bought in the supermarket. Supermarkets demand a uniform and even product within precise weight

Modern meat hybrids, such as this Cobb 700, are specialist birds that require careful management, and aren't ideally suited to the DIY environment.

ranges. As a consequence of these requirements, the poultry farmer has been forced into producing birds that meet these strict guidelines.

Slow cooking

Home-produced birds will certainly be less uniform in size and shape, and will present darker-coloured thigh and leg meat. The flesh will also be much denser, meaning that it'll take longer to cook than the typical supermarket item. This is because the bones of a standard-bred bird are more fully developed, and much denser. You're also likely to find that the sinews in the legs will have developed more too, and these can either be removed when dressing, or pulled out when cooked.

However, the real pleasure comes in the taste. Home-reared poultry should taste like chicken used to taste (for those of you who can remember it!). They will have a stronger, more satisfying flavour than the insipid, shop-bought alternative.

When you're happy that your birds have reached the desired size for your purposes, the best advice is to remove the feeding trough from the shed at least the night before killing. By doing this you'll ensure that their crops are empty and that there will be less faecal matter in the alimental tract. You'll appreciate both of these facts when it comes to the dressing stage! Sensible measures like this are essential to help minimise the risk of meat contamination.

There's really no comparison between shop-bought and home-reared chicken in terms of flavour, although home-reared is likely to need more cooking as it tends to be denser.

Pastured poultry

Scott Franklin describes pastured broilers, an environmentally and welfare-friendly approach to the rearing of hybrid meat birds

While nothing special to look at, these 'pasture raised' hybrids are very impressive converters of feed into meat.

For many poultry keepers, the idea of regarding their chickens as a source of food is a disconcerting one. However, for those of you prepared to take a slightly more practical viewpoint, there are tremendous benefits to be enjoyed.

Of course, the chicken straddles the boundary between a domestic pet and working livestock, which is surely one of the reasons why keeping them is so popular with so many people. But it's the adaptability of the chicken, from a breeding point of view, which has allowed all manner of variations to be produced, giving rise to everything from the pampered Pekin to the heavyweight broiler.

In terms of meat production, the specialised broiler breeds are second to none. Only fish, to the best of my knowledge, are more efficient converters of energy from feedstuffs into final product, meat. The ratio of energy in versus energy out can be as low as 2:1; roughly speaking, two pounds of feed for one pound of bird. To put this in perspective, pigs work on a ratio of about 5:1 and beef cattle around 7:1. Good dairy cows – one of my favorites – can get close to a 2:1 ratio where milk is concerned.

The other big advantage of the production broiler is the speed with which it grows. Modern development has reduced the hatch-to-butcher-shop time from 16 weeks back in the 1930s, to just 40 days now; less than six weeks! While this fact obviously won't sit happily with plenty of traditional hobby keepers, it is quite phenomenal nonetheless, in my view. By selecting for the fastest-growing birds – basically the ones with an appetite that won't quit and a very docile nature – breeders have developed a bird that reaches half its mature size in just six or seven weeks.

One might think it kindness to spare a few of these gentle birds, and raise them to maturity. But this isn't as easy as it sounds. The commercial meat breeds are, understandably, predisposed to fat and, unless they're raised on a very strict diet, the big danger is fatal heart attack. Also, to get eggs from a broiler hen is a bit of a challenge because if you limit the feed too much, she'll simply refuse to lay. Give too much, on the other hand, and you'll more than likely find her on her back one morning. It's a delicate balancing act.

In the past two decades, perhaps because the birds are being pushed for ever more rapid growth (greater profits), the chicken in our supermarkets has become fatter, to the point that it's now not very nice. It's this unfortunate trend, which set me on the track of rearing my own pastured broilers.

Here in the United States there's a definite trend towards increasing numbers of small producer/farmers growing birds in open-bottomed pens on grass pasture. It's rapidly becoming as popular as organic-raised food, and is probably healthier. One man, Joel Salatin from the Shenandoah Valley region of Virginia, has been very influential. He's a farmer and first class marketeer who pretty much pioneered the method here, pasturing egg layers and beef cattle as well as broilers sequentially; the beef cows and calves behind the

Joe Salatin, who devised this DIY approach to home-reared meat bird, operates on a pretty large scale.

broilers, and the hens behind the beefers. The idea was that one should follow the other in a symbiotic way, demonstrating how to make a good living in a very environmentally-friendly way. There's now an American Pastured Poultry Producers Association, the APPPA, with an excellent website (www.apppa.org).

I've tried the method several times over the past few years, evolving it to the point where, last autumn, I was reasonably successful and satisfied with the results. What follows is my adaptation of Joel Salatin's process.

First of all, the chicken eats a lot

of grass. Joel estimates the intake to be as much as 30% of the diet. How accurate this is is difficult to know for certain, but it's certainly a high proportion. When you move the pen, the first thing the birds do is run ahead to chow down on the fresh grass. Their digestive tract is adapted to digest grass; the natural carotinoid pigments in the vegetation are transferred to their fat, skin, and egg yolks. Consequently, providing free-range grass like this means that you (1) offer a healthier diet than that provided by grain-based feed alone, and (2) you save on feed costs.

In addition, the birds get more

My own moveable pen is based on Joe's original, with modifications suitable for my needs and situation.

exercise, don't lay down fat as quickly and, ultimately, develop into a firmer-fleshed, better tasting end product. This is especially so if you limit the feed slightly, and keep them growing a little longer to, say, eight or nine weeks. By that time you'll have dressed pullets averaging over five pounds, and cockerels of up to eight pounds; a good meal!

The advantage to the land is a dramatic increase in fertility, and an actual creation of topsoil. The pasture will never require plowing. The grass responds so favorably to poultry manure that it soon chokes out the competition, and provides enough growth for excellent grazing and an occasional cutting of hay. This is the symbiotic effect that Joel capitalises on. While the input is in the broiler and layer feed, the output is measured in the excellent broilers, the beef produced, the high-quality eggs, and significantly deeper topsoil. Joel hasn't plowed his two 50-acre pastures in over 40 years and, in that time, the topsoil has regenerated to pre-Civil War levels. I can testify personally to the lush growth of grass there; it's like a very deep lawn!

The pens Joel uses are built to his own design, and measure 10x12'. They are two feet high and built cheaply from light timber (2x2" and 1x2" sections), with a lightweight aluminum sheet roof covering. The framework is covered with chicken wire, of course, and all joints are secured with cheap, drywall screws. Joel figures this size pen works best for about 85 growing broilers.

Naturally, I've done things a little differently; I like to experiment! My first pen, with wheels, was way too heavy for one man to move. But they got better. My third attempt was a 12x16' monster, high enough to almost stand up in. I could move it; half a PVC pipe fastened under the trailing edge, riding on two long pieces of 2x2" timber to break friction with the ground.

My most recent attempt, here at our new home, is the best yet. A little larger than

Here I am with a couple of my grandchildren, about to carve.

Joel's, and still a bit heavier, but it serves my purposes. I used two 3'x12' sheets of metal roofing left over from an earlier project to cover the sides of the top. Two wire frame doors run up the center so I can see if I'm about to run over anybody with the trailing edge as it's being moved. It's two-and-a-half feet high, so I can get in and out and move around easily inside. I used three-foot, vinyl-coated, one-inch poultry netting (far more durable than non-coated) for the sides, leaving six inches off the bottom making it easier to secure the gaps on uneven ground. Also, I no longer use drywall screws; they rust out in about 18 months flat but, thankfully, there are much better alternatives available. I've also found that plenty of diagonal bracing makes for a reasonably sturdy pen which should last at least three or four years. To break friction with the ground, I dado-cut (a groove cut into one piece of wood

This is what it's all about!

into which another piece of wood will fit snugly) two, four-inch PVC end caps to fit under the trailing edge, so the pen rides on the slick caps when it's being moved.

I start the chicks in my two ancient battery brooders, 50 in each. They need to be moved out after about 10 days, as their rate of growth begins to increase exponentially. In good weather you can move them right outside as early as 12 days. The heat of metabolism from their feed seems to provide all the heat they need at this point, and they share the warmth at night by snuggling close together.

The early growth determines largely how well-grown a bird you will have at eight weeks so, yes, it's very important to start them off right. Also they learn to eat grass early on. It's critical to fast these chicks after the first week, at least for overnight, every day. They are much less prone to heart attacks and, in the last few weeks, you can regulate the amount of fat they are laying down. By doing this you'll still get a very meaty bird, just with less fat. I should also mention that these broiler birds never pick at each other unlike other breeds; one less thing to worry about.

My pen design, open though it is, is still very effective at keeping the birds dry in wet weather. This surprised me, in fact, but I had no problem with wet chickens. The manure is absorbed into the soil very rapidly, and I only keep the birds on any one particular 10x12' plot for a single day; thus protecting the grass. You can see the difference in grass colour and growth where the pen has been. Grass thrives on grazing; it's designed to continue growing, incorporating available nutrients quickly. This method of fertilisation is much better than composting, although I'm sure many people aren't aware of this. The composting process actually removes valuable nutrients through the oxidation process and the final product, while good for improving soil tilth and sweet-smelling, is actually low in nutrition. •

A poultryman's winter diary

Andy Marshall reveals some of his winter routines that help him with successful egg incubation

Weather plays an important part in successful fertility, and each part of the year requires adaptations to routines. The constant dark, damp days of winter are not very conducive to fertile eggs, so we endeavour to combat this with a range of chicken Viagra tonics!

Sprouted grains, crisp cabbage and Swedes are on the menu. Whole wheat and oats are soaked overnight in warm water, then drained and spread into seed trays in the warm greenhouse. Here it sits for about four days, after which it's fed to the birds. It is important to introduce this gradually to avoid any digestive upsets, so start by mixing a little in the afternoon feed and then, over a week, it can virtually replace the wheat feed.

Any fresh, winter greens (cabbage, cauliflower etc) are adored by the birds. Hang the plants upside-down on a string, setting them at just above the birds' heads, so that they have to stretch to eat them. However, don't under any circumstances feed them stale or limp greens, as these will cause digestive problems such as compacted crop. If the brassicas are from the garden, then split the stalks once the birds have eaten the leaves; they'll really enjoy eating the soft pith inside.

Swedes are another much-enjoyed tit-bit. Split the roots and leave for the birds to pick clean before collecting the empty skins for the compost heap. Also, don't forget that grit is an essential condiment when feeding greens and roots, as it's required by the gizzard to assist with grinding-up the food.

Sometimes frost lingers throughout the morning, and comes down again by 4pm in the afternoon. Fertile eggs, if chilled or frosted, won't develop in an incubator, so always try to collect them as quickly as possible, storing them in clean egg trays. They are all marked with a soft pencil (eg. 'LS' for Light Sussex, 'SG' for Scots Grey), since pencil seems to best resist the egg wash before before the eggs are set in the incubator. Marking eggs is important as it indicates if the male is fertile, or if he is favouring one hen rather than the whole pen.

These routines are vital for successful poultry breeding. Hatching eggs are always placed point-down in clean egg trays, with different trays being used for each day of the week. Every Saturday the eggs are washed and left to dry in plastic egg trays then, on Sunday morning, set in the incubator. Every Sunday evening I make a point of taking a glass of wine with me up to the incubator room, and carefully candle all the eggs that have been in the machines for a week. The wine is either to celebrate good fertility, or drown my sorrows! Remember that the fertility of poultry eggs drops off dramatically in eggs that are more than ten days old, so never leave them hanging around for longer than this if you can help it.

A soft pencil offers the simplest and most durable way of marking eggs for hatching. A methodical approach like this is vital as part of a successful breeding program.

By setting the eggs on a Sunday, hatching always starts on a Friday, and the chicks are ready to go out on Sunday morning. This means that we never have chicks needing to be moved out of the incubator on a week day, and have more time to toe-punch and identify the chicks as they go to the brooder house. Another advantage of this simple system is that moving the chicks into the brooder house in the morning gives them the rest of the day to settle into their new surroundings.

We use a Mayfair Aliwal incubator. This machine is, to my mind, the best on the market, as you're able to hatch and set eggs each week. Even the smallest in the range has three trays, giving you much-needed flexibility. •

Don't forget to make grit available to your birds, especially if you're also feeding them fresh greens – it's essential for effective food break-down in the gizzard.

Good call

What about hatching and rearing ducks? Ian Kay introduces the diminutive yet highly attractive and much-fanced Call duck – a breed that he especially recommends to families with children

One of the most popular breed of waterfowl at the time of writing is the Call duck. During the past decade this curvaceous little bird has captivated the imagination of both exhibitors and the general poultry keeper alike.

What's more, thanks to some dedicated and exceptionally skilled breeding from experienced keepers, the standard of perfection within the breed is now at an all-time high. Consequently, competition among a whole range of popular Call duck colours is extremely high also.

What a charmer!
People newly attracted to keeping these charming

Blue Fawn Call ducks.

little birds could be excused for thinking that they are a recent addition to this country's waterfowl breed listing, but this simply isn't the case. The Call duck is actually very well established here, and has been around in Great Britain for several centuries. During this time the bird has often been referred to as the 'Decoy Duck'; a term which arose because of the Call's ability to live in a confined area of water, and call in other types of wild ducks, which were then caught in nets and often used in the catering trade. These original birds are thought to have arrived here from Holland, which is where many of today's foundation stock birds have also originated.

Their arrival in Holland was originally from the East Indies. At this period there were only two colours of Calls; pure White and the Mallard, which is usually called Grey.

Despite the breed's evident popularity, it's quite rare to read practical advice aimed at those interested in getting started with Calls, so that's what I intend to provide here. The price of these beautiful little birds varies greatly, as does their showing potential. Consequently, my advice to new keepers is that it's sensible to make a decision at an early stage about your fundamental reason for keeping.

If you wish to exhibit Call ducks at the highest level, then you'll have to be prepared to pay a lot of money for your foundation stock and, even then, appreciate that success in the show pen can never be guaranteed. Selecting good stock to buy requires a good knowledge of the breed, and the points where they must excel to be able to make an impact at the premier shows.

Conversely, if your attraction to these birds is purely because you want the pleasure of enjoying their company in your garden, or on a pond, and you have no ambition to enter the show arena, then the situation is a good deal more straightforward. Not having to buy birds bred closely to the breed standard can be an advantage to overall health. Getting birds that are slightly longer in the bill, and a bit stronger in body size, tends to make them less prone to sinus problems and more resistant to adverse weather conditions. Greater all-round strength can also make them more resistant to disease too.

What's more, if you're interested in breeding from your Calls, then it's worth noting that larger-bodied examples will be perfectly capable of laying 50 eggs in a season. Also, the greater size and strength of bigger Calls will mean there's a reduced chance of losing females because they have become 'egg bound' or suffered a prolapse. This type of Call can be bought for a very modest price, and should be available in the full range of colours that have now been created.

Good mixer?

However, if you're not keen on hatching birds, and simply want to own adult examples as ornamental pets, then you also have the option of keeping a male-only group. As with most other species of livestock, it tends to be the males which display the most pronounced colourings, and this is certainly the case with Call ducks. The drakes are far more decorative than their duck equivalents, making them the more attractive option from a purely visual point of view.

Also, in case you're worried about how a group of male birds will get on together, you'll have few problems as long as you maintain a strictly male-only environment. They'll live together in peace and harmony throughout the year, thus allowing you to admire their attractive and varied colourings without the problem of males arguing between themselves over the choice of a female.

Surplus Call drakes can usually be bought at very reasonable prices; it's usually single females that are in short supply, and hard to obtain.

As I mentioned before, if your heart is set on showing, then great care is needed when buying birds. The Call duck is a breed where comparative judging is reasonably easy; that's when the birds are placed side by side. However, I know of many instances where the top birds in a group (or in a class at a

Butterscotch Calls.

Mandarin and Carolina Call ducks.

Silver Call ducks.

Female Yellowbelly Call duck.

small show) look to be excellent, but when placed alongside the ones at a show of higher status suddenly start to look very ordinary!

Careful breeding

A point to bear in mind if you intend to produce show quality Calls is that the best results are obtained when breeding from a pair of birds that share the same bloodline. If two entirely different strains are paired together, it's quite common for their offspring to gain hybrid vigour, with the resulting first generation of birds being larger and more coarse in structure than their parents. This, will usually mean that they're unsuitable as exhibition candidates. Of course, they could be used as future breeders and, with careful selection, it might be possible to attain the correct type over several generations.

Whatever your reasons for keeping Calls, the birds themselves are very adaptable to different types of surroundings, and don't require elaborate housing or especially high levels of husbandry. A small area of water in something like an old sink or childrens' bath, where they can splash about and enjoy a good playtime, is their main requirement. Their diet can be poultry pellets, plus a little whole wheat and, of course, all the household scraps and surplus titbits.

If you're in a family situation, a group of Call ducks can offer a great advantage over the more conventional chicken or bantam alternatives. Their beaks are well-rounded and, therefore, the risk of a young child getting hurt by being pecked is greatly reduced while giving these cute little birds a cuddle.

You can also ensure plenty of visual interest thanks to the wide range of plumage options, many of which are illustrated here. Lots of these have been developed and introduced in recent years, and the process of colour standardisation is ongoing. As you'll notice, the colour choices include intriguingly-named varieties, such as the Yellowbelly, the Chocolate and the Butterscotch. There are also a number of variations of the Silver colouring plus, of course, the ever-popular Apricot.

But whichever you finally decide on, you can rest assured that this desirable little breed will bring you and your family many happy hours of pleasure and interest in the garden. •

Crooked neck

Terry Beebe highlights an unfortunate and unpleasant condition that most commonly affects young crested breeds such as the Poland and the Silkie

This shocking condition, known variously as 'cerebral hernia', 'Crooked neck' and even 'Seahorse syndrome' is an unpleasant one, and no keeper is going to enjoy dealing with. But it's as well to be prepared for it, particularly if you are a poultry enthusiast who enjoys breeding some of our most popular crested breeds, including the Poland and Silkie.

Although I've seen breeds such as the Leghorn affected by this problem on very rare occasions, it tends to be far more likely to afflict breeds which carry a crested head which, in turn, is created by a domed skull. Most obvious among these are the Poland and the Silkie. These two, in my experience, are certainly far more at risk of suffering from this awful condition than those with more conventionally-shaped heads.

I've certainly experienced this problem myself with my own Polands and, although it doesn't seem to be as frequent now as it was a few years ago, we still see the occasional bird that's cast down by this strange problem.

Crooked cure?

Over the years I've tried several different ways of treating this problem but, to be honest, I haven't really been able to claim any great success with any of them. I've experimented with the use of vitamin supplements, heat lamps and even gentle massage, but never with any degree of consistency in terms of the results achieved. Certainly there has been the odd success story, but these are the exceptions. Usually, I'm sorry to say, the end is not a happy one for the birds involved.

One of the leading authorities on this problem, as it relates to Silkies, is Sue Bowser. Sue has been a successful breeder and exhibitor, and closely associated with the Silkie Club for years. Consequently, she is a mine of information on this problem, and has plenty of anecdotal accounts relating to both its occurrence and effects. While chatting with her during my research for this feature, she told me about a case she'd heard about which fairly typically illustrates the way in which the problem strikes.

A Silkie Club member got in touch about a problem she'd noticed with one of her birds. This particular blue Silkie was reluctant to leave the poultry house, and when it was removed by hand later in the day, was found to be showing early signs of a slightly bent neck. This became worse fairly rapidly and, by the following day, the bird's neck was quite badly arched and twisted. The owner encouraged the bird to stand, but all that happened was that it rolled over on to its back, and the neck remained twisted. This happened repeatedly and was, as you might imagine, very distressing for all concerned.

At this point Sue advised the owner to take the bird to the vet and request that it be treated with both cortisone and a product called Baytril. The vet took the opportunity to consult directly with Sue, and agreed upon this treatment combination, even though they both concluded that the problem was being caused by water on the brain.

The cortisone was injected and a 2.5% solution of Baytril was added to the drinking water (at a dosage of 2ml per litre) for a period of seven days. It should be noted here that Baytril is a prescription-only medicine that's only available from a vet. It offers no guarantee of a cure in cases like this but, in my view, is certainly worth a go if your vet can be convinced. In this particular instance, the bird was lucky and, after a short period of treatment, it made a miraculous and complete recovery.

Although the results in this case were extremely encouraging, this shouldn't really be taken as the norm. In reality the 'cerebral hernia' condition is usually both incurable and terminal. For this reason it's very important that birds which have suffered with this problem to any degree aren't used as part of a breeding program. I believe that an increased tendency towards to this condition is passed to the offspring.

Bone structure

The Silkie and Poland breeds have a different type of skull formation to other, more traditional types of chicken. The Silkie has what's known as a 'vaulted skull', while the Poland is characterised by its 'poll'. Both of these descriptions relate to the dome or raised section on the top of the skull, from which the crest feathers grow. These skull formations are easily seen when the chicks are a day old but, during these early days especially, this bone structure is very soft. Consequently, stray pecking or a knock on the head can easily damage this thin bony layer, causing all sorts of undesirable problems for the brain inside. It can swell and, in extreme cases, become herniated and ooze out through a damaged section. This is obviously very serious, and is bound to cause

Young crested breeds – such as this Silkie – seem most prone to this strange brain-related problem at around the four-months mark.

the bird all sorts of problems, including balance issues.

Research on both these famous crested breeds has linked their raised skulls with an increased incidence of twisted neck syndrome, although any more specific explanatory information than this is difficult to track down. A few cases which have been subject to a post mortem examination have shown the birds suffering with a hydrocephalus condition (water on the brain), and also that sections of the brain were actually exposed inside the skull.

In my experience, the severity of

Another typical at-risk breed is the Poland, but this silver-laced frizzle is safe – it's an adult

the condition can vary. Some birds may begin by developing a mild form of head wobbling, which then gradually worsens until the head becomes completely twisted around, or is forced down under the body, between the legs. Birds suffering like this will quickly lose all mobility, and I certainly think that some of these will have been wrongly diagnosed as having Marek's disease in the past.

Encountering this problem is certainly very unpleasant, but seems to be something which keepers of these fine, crested breeds have to come to terms with. If you're a serious breeder of Silkies or Polands, then you'll have to use your breeding records to keep track of the lines which seem to have been most prone to it. You can also help reduce the tendency by introducing new blood to your strain from an outcross. As well as this, I try to always make sure that the breeding lines are varied on a regular basis, to further reduce the risks.

Be prepared

For those keepers at the more 'domestic' end of the scale who tend not to be so precise with their record keeping, all I can suggest is that you remain aware of this possibility, and act swiftly if you have any concerns. It has been suggested that one influencing factor can be a vitamin imbalance. I've experimented with this idea, by giving affected birds additional vitamin B and C doses and, while I've had some encouraging results, I can't honestly say that this represents a cure – sometimes it works, sometimes it doesn't. The truth is that there's currently no proven cure. Once the damage has been done to the brain, be it caused by genetic defect, physical impact damage or fluid build-up, there's unfortunately no way of putting it right with any useful degree of consistency.

The most important thing to bear in mind is that we all have a duty of care to the birds we look after. It's our responsibility to do all we can to minimise the amount of suffering caused, so it's vital to seek professional advice at the earliest opportunity, or to cull the bird yourself if you're sure that a recovery is out of the question. •

Separating the sexes

Bob Cross looks at the phenomenon of sex-linkage, and the ways in which it can be usefully employed in the world of poultry

Chicks of all poultry species hatch in roughly equal proportions of male and female but, depending on their destination and purpose, there can be more of a demand for one sex than the other.

The obvious example is egg production, where only females are required, and the same idea applies to the meat breeds where males are the preferred choice for the seasonal market. So, with this in mind, the ability to determine the sex of a chick at day-old has clear advantages, allowing us to identify those we want to keep so that maximum effort and resources can be focused on them alone.

However, sexing day-old chicks isn't as easy as you might imagine in most cases. Generally, most young chicks look much about the same outwardly and, if there are any differences, they're subtle. The exception to this rule, of course, are the sex-linked crosses which present various, clear contrasts which usefully differentiate between the sexes.

Weighty issues
The subtle differences I mentioned include day-old chick weight; the males being marginally heavier than females. However, the weight of the chick is more influenced by

the egg size than anything else, so there will be heavier pullets from bigger eggs and vice versa. In any case, these differences will be so small as to make it impossible to determine the sex this way with any degree of consistent accuracy.

Down colour and pattern is of more use but, once again, this has its limitations. It's only really useful for certain breeds, and then only if the keeper has reasonable knowledge and experience of the breed involved. On hatching, the chicks of barred black breeds such as Plymouth Rock show predominantly black down with varying amounts of grey/creamy white on the abdomen, plus a similarly-coloured spot on the back of the head. The shanks also contain dark pigment. At day-old the females will be darker overall, and have smaller head spots than the males.

The head spots will likely be oval with the long axis running down the neck, while those on the male will be larger and irregular. The shanks of the female are darker, and the pigment stops sharply at toe level, while those on the males are paler and show no line of distinction between the black pigment of the shanks and the yellow of the toes.

Differences in down pattern have been noted in Rhode Island Red and New Hampshire Red chicks, where there is evidence of stripes and spots in the down. Researchers (Byerly and Quinn, 1936) found that most striped chicks – and those with spots of black down at the back of the head – were likely to be female. Homer Rowell, at Massachusetts, worked with the Rhode Island Red and revealed another method; when the wings of the day-old chick are outstretched, the down colour of the females is uniformly red in colour while that of the male features white streaks of varying size on the web.

Jaap confirmed the success of this method in 1946. He stated that

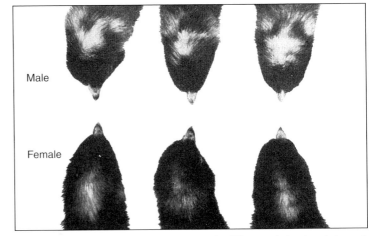

Barred Plymouth Rock chick heads illustrating the differences in head spot size and shape.

an accuracy of between 90-95% in RIR and 80-90% in NHR was attainable, adding that it required chicks that are uniformly red on the head and back, and males that themselves had showed large white wing spots as day-olds.

Chicks of breeds of the 'wild type', or black-breasted, red plumage pattern such as the Brown Leghorn, hatch with down that presents light and dark longitudinal stripes. In 1946 MacArthur and MacIlraith showed that, with some practice, chicks of these breeds could be accurately sexed. The females being darker in general,

having a wider middle stripe down the back, and tending to be darker in the face than the males. The females also show a stripe over the eye, through the ear to the neck, that's not easily seen in the males.

While the examples we've given are obviously of use to those breeders who keep the those breeds, it's worth bearing in mind that even what seem to be the cut-and-dried sexing methods mentioned above should nevertheless be practised with caution. In practice, it takes a great deal of prior study, recording and selection of the particular strain

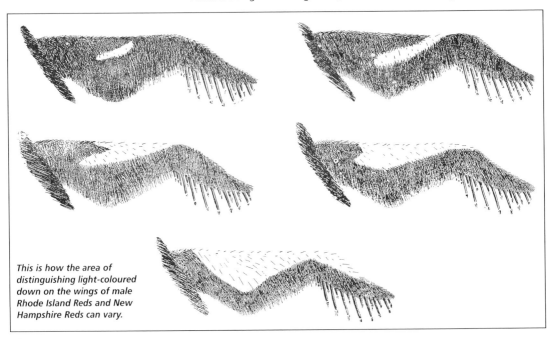

This is how the area of distinguishing light-coloured down on the wings of male Rhode Island Reds and New Hampshire Reds can vary.

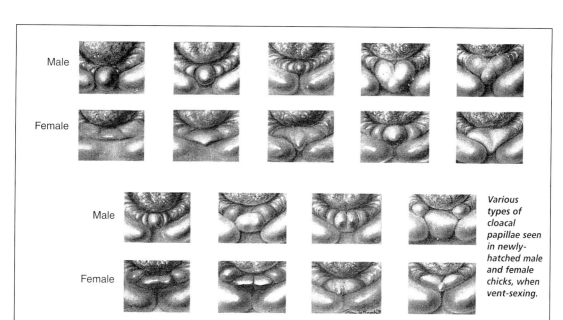

Male

Female

Male

Female

Various types of cloacal papillae seen in newly-hatched male and female chicks, when vent-sexing.

involved before anyone can start to become truly confident about sexing these sorts of young chick with reliable accuracy.

Alternative method

Vent sexing is the other method of sexing chicks. It can be used on any breed or cross, and was first demonstrated to the West in 1933; it had been extensively practised in Japan and China long before then. In simple terms, it involves examination (with the naked eye) of the genital papilla or eminence on the ventral surface of the cloaca, inside the vent. In the male this is seen as a rudimentary copulatory organ but, in the female, it is absent or sufficiently different in shape or size to allow the sex of the chick to be identified. The examination should take place under bright, diffused light, and requires first class eyesight and dexterity.

The chick is held upside down, the vent is gently opened and, in the few seconds it's held like this, a decision has to be made. If the papilla is obviously pronounced then the chick is likely to be a cockerel. If it appears smooth, flat, hollow, soft or weak, it's most likely a pullet. About 80% of the chicks appear clearly male or female when examined, but the remainder are difficult to determine *(see illustration, above, of the possible variation).*

GENETIC FUNDAMENTALS

Sex determination

Sex in poultry is determined by the presence of sex chromosomes; in the case of the male or cockerel, it has two whereas the female or pullet only has one, the other is either missing or modified to a point where it's not functional.

The gametes (the sperm or the egg), the male or female contribution to the next generation, only possess half the chromosome number (haploid). However, when they come together and fuse at conception, the number is once again restored to its normal (diploid) state.

In the case of chickens all sperm contain a sex chromosome, but there are two types of eggs, those with a sex chromosome and those without. At conception if a sperm meets with an egg that contains a sex chromosome the resultant chick will possess two and will be male. If it meets an egg that doesn't contain one, the resultant chick will only have one and will be female.

Dominant and recessive characters

Certain characters are dominant over others, for the purpose of this

The ability to carry out this sort of vent sexing is best learned 'hands-on' under the guidance of

exercise it's right to assume that dominant characters will assert their influence over the recessive ones. Over the years much work has been carried out to establish which characters are dominant over which others. They are referred to using letters, with a capital denoting dominance.

Genotype
The genetic make-up of a bird.

Phenotype
The physical appearance of the bird; birds that look the same for a character have the same phenotype, but may have a different genotype.

Homozygous
Genetically pure.

Heterozygous
Genetically impure.

Hemizygous
This term refers to the state of purity in the female where, because it only has the one sex chromosome, it can't be impure but, likewise, neither can it be classified as homozygous.

an expert and, even then, it takes years of practice with thousands of chicks to become proficient.

Professional sexers can sex several hundred chicks an hour with an accuracy exceeding 95%, but it's not likely to be an option for the domestic poultry keeper.

At one time, chick sexing machines were available. These were effectively an endoscope-cum-microscope with an illuminated probe made to exacting proportions to ensure correct positioning inside the chick. For ease of handling it was shaped like a pistol, and its use involved inserting the probe through the vent and up along the intestine. A light shone through the intestine revealing the presence of testes or an ovary. Viewed through the eyepiece of the machine, the magnified image gave a clear view of the tiny organs. This operation is best carried out on very fresh chicks, where the wall of the intestine is still fairly transparent. However, both of these methods require handling and manipulation of delicate creatures, at a time in their life when they can do without additional stresses and, as such, really are best left to the experts.

Sex-linkage

Sex-linkage is the association of a character or trait with the sex of an animal. Although it's likely that poultry keepers had made use of it for many years, the science behind it wasn't fully understood until the early part of the 20th century, when two men from Cambridge – Professor RC Punnet and Mr MS Pease – offered an explanation. However, before embarking on their explanation, it's probably as well to spend a few minutes considering the basic explanations provided in the 'Genetic fundamentals' box.

Punnet and Pease' ideas went along the following lines. Carried on the sex chromosome are genes for other characters; in poultry the most common application for sex-linkage is for feather or down colour, the genes for silver or gold plumage being carried on the sex chromosomes. All chickens are one or the other. Unfortunately, they don't all appear as such. For example, black ones could be either silver or gold, and the only way to find out is by experimentation or referring to previous studies. Other

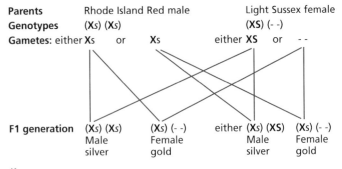

RHODE ISLAND RED CROSSED WITH LIGHT SUSSEX PULLET

The Rhode Island Red is genetically gold and appears a reddish-brown all over. The Light Sussex is genetically silver; it's a white bird with a black tail, wing flights and neck hackles.

Parents Rhode Island Red male Light Sussex female
Genotypes (Xs) (Xs) (XS) (- -)
Gametes: either Xs or Xs either XS or - -

F1 generation (Xs) (Xs) (Xs) (- -) either (Xs) (XS) (Xs) (- -)
 Male Female Male Female
 silver gold silver gold

Key
X presence of a sex chromosome
- - absence of a sex chromosome
S silver (dominant)
s gold (recessive)

Colour differences in chicks produced by a Rhode Island Red cock crossed with a Light Sussex hen – the female is on the right.

Cuckoo barred feather patterning, rate of feathering and shank colour.

Sex-linkage breeds

Traditionally, the most popular cross exploiting sex-linkage was that using a Rhode Island Red cockerel mated to a Light Sussex female; the Rhode carrying the gene for gold and the Sussex the one for silver (refer to diagram). Other gold carriers include the New Hampshire Red and the red, brown or buff varieties of a number of other breeds. The silver gene is carried by many white or silver varieties.

the result of either a Rhode Island Red or New Hampshire Red being mated to a White Plymouth Rock. The female side of the cross must always carry the dominant gene.

Phenotypes

It will be seen that the males are all silver and the females gold. At day-old all the male chicks appear a pale creamy yellow, while the females are brown. If a buff breed is used instead of the RIR, the resultant chicks will be paler. This can lead to a few problems in identifying borderline cases of darker-downed males and lighter females. This is made even worse in incubators where formaldehyde is used as a fumigant in the hatching stage, because it deepens the yellow down colour.

Genotypes

Although all the males are silver, they are heterozygous; in other words, they contain the genes for both silver and gold. However, because the silver is dominant, that's how they appear. The females have only the gold gene attached to the one sex chromosome. As the other one is missing, it cannot carry the colour gene and, therefore, have any influence. Note also that this is an example of the hemizygous state.

Dabbling with ducks

Gail Harland, an experienced chicken keeper, decided to branch out into ducks – and loved every minute of it!

I'd kept chickens for over ten years before I succumbed to the lure of ducks. Actually, ducks are such comical and characterful creatures that it's a wonder that I'd been able to resist for so long! We even have a pond in our garden, but I'd always worried about introducing ducks to it because it tends to quickly get overgrown with reed mace, and has a tendency to dry out in hot summers.

However, after visiting the Domestic Fowl Trust in Gloucestershire, where I saw that

ducks can live quite happily even without a spacious pond of their own to swim in, I decided to go ahead and purchase some. We have a large area of grass at the back of the garage that I thought would make a good duck pen; it was already surrounded by a sturdy picket fence.

A visit to the East of England Autumn Show at Peterborough solved the water issue, as we found a stall selling attractive duck baths. At about 70cm in diameter, they were big enough for a duck to get

in and completely immerse its head to keep the feathers in good condition, and yet small and light enough to ensure that a daily change of the water is not an onerous task that would get neglected. But the first job was to think about a house that would keep the ducks safe from nocturnal visits by the fox.

Housing choice
There's a wide range of duck arks available commercially, with prices starting from around £100. When

comparing prices, you do need to remember to include the delivery charges, which I found can increase the final price dramatically. However, we had a garage full of timber off-cuts, so I persuaded my teenage sons to spend a half-term holiday building me a duck house. The result was a house about 70cm square, built to look like a castle, with a drawbridge that lowers to be used as a ramp during the day but lockable at night to keep the house fox-proof.

The roof is made from some leftover corrugated plastic sheeting – Onduline is a modern, split-resistant alternative available from builders' merchants. We keep the house well raised above the ground on brick supports, so that rats aren't tempted to nest underneath. A house this size is only suitable for a pair of light breed ducks, but I was fortunate in that we also had a large, brick and timber playhouse that the boys no longer used which would make an ideal duck house.

With two houses sorted, the next stage was to decide which were to be my starter breeds. Any of the big poultry shows provide a great opportunity to view a good assortment of breeds, so that you can see which ones you like the look of. Just as important is the sound; some ducks are much noisier than others. My youngest son loved the look of the little Call ducks that we saw at the East of England Show but the females, in particular, are very noisy, so this may not be a suitable breed if you have close neighbours.

I fell in love with some Bali ducks, which look like a crested version of the Indian Runner. Research on the internet brought up the website of the Domestic Waterfowl Club (www.domestic-waterfowl.co.uk) which warns that Balis are not a 'beginner's duck'. Like other crested breeds, they have a lethal crested gene, which means that they're difficult to breed, with a higher than average proportion of dead-in-shell ducklings. However, while I obviously appreciated the warning, I'm not sure that I agree that some birds are unsuitable for beginners; the implication being that you should 'practice' first on a breed that you don't necessarily want. I'm inclined to think you

Our old, brick-based children's playhouse was pressed into service as accommodation for the two chocolate Muscovies.

should go with your heart, so long as you're prepared to fully research the care of your chosen breed. After all, I'm sure that if you keep animals that really interest you, you're more likely to expend the necessary time and effort in their care.

What else?
Another breed that interested me was the Muscovy. Unlike all other breeds of domestic ducks, the Muscovy isn't descended from the

wild mallard duck, but is a distinct species that originated in Central and South America. They are very quiet birds but full of character, with a tendency to nod their heads enthusiastically and wag their tails like dogs! I was particularly taken with the picture of a chocolate-coloured Muscovy duck in Storey's *Illustrated Guide to Poultry Breeds*; a book I was given as a birthday present.

So, having decided that I was

Cleaning-out is a simple and speedy operation. The Bali and Muscovy houses' floors are both covered with newspaper plus a layer of straw, and this is changed on a weekly basis.

going to start with a pair of white Balis and a pair of chocolate Muscovies, I rang Nick Willis of Anglia Wildfowl – which is just a ten-minute drive from where I live in Suffolk. By lucky chance, he had exactly those birds available, so I was able to pick them up the very next week.

I can thoroughly recommend getting your first ducks direct from a breeder as, by doing so, you can really benefit from their advice and expertise. Nick was able to demonstrate how best to catch and carry an uncooperative duck (he suggests holding them under the wings, at the 'shoulders' as, after millions of years of evolution for flying, these are the strongest joints). He also showed me how to clip the Muscovies' flight feathers, so that I could let them free-range in the garden without worrying about them flying off to the local lake.

I was warned that ducks are less likely than chickens to put themselves away in their house at night although, as it transpired, the Balis decided to prove me wrong. After being kept in for the first day, they routinely went back into the house each night. Given the chance, the Muscovies like to stay out later, and will wait until it's really dark before putting themselves away. But I usually round them up at dusk.

Both pairs of ducks settled in well, and really seemed to enjoy each others' company. As soon as the Muscovies were let out in the morning, they rushed over to the Balis' pen to greet them through the picket fence. There's always an amusing example of the grass being greener on the other side of the fence, as the Muscovies tried to eat the grass inside the pen while the Balis – inside the pen – would stick their necks out to eat the grass outside! I was a little concerned that the large Muscovy drake might bully my chickens but, thankfully, he showed no interest in them, and even tended to move out of the way of the Sultan cockerel. I'm hopeful that they'll all continue to live together harmoniously.

Down to earth

At a practical level, ducks really don't require too much attention; I feed them layers pellets first thing in the morning then, after taking

I've been advised that this is one of the best ways to carry an adult duck.

the boys to school, I change their water. The Muscovies have a large cat litter tray as a bath in their house, which the drake virtually fills when he gets in! But they don't use it much and have never been to investigate the garden pond. They get a handful of grain each after school – I've been using mixed grain (always bought for the chickens), but I've noticed that the white Balis

This is the 70cm duck bath used by the Balis; the water is changed every day.

are taking on a distinctly yellow tinge, presumably from the maize in the mixed corn, so I have now started to use just wheat.

Cleaning out both houses takes me less than half an hour. The smaller house, which has a removable back, is easy to keep clean because I line it with an opened-out, broadsheet newspaper topped with a layer of straw. I began by lining the Muscovy's 'playhouse' with big sheets of cardboard but, having exhausted my supply, now use newspapers in there too. I give them a fresh bed every week, which consists of a cardboard melon box from the supermarket, lined with straw. The old bedding and newspapers are added to our compost heaps.

One thing I have noticed is that ducks are undoubtedly messier than chickens. Their droppings are much more liquid but, with just a few to look after in my case, they haven't been a problem. Unlike chickens, they don't make dust baths wherever you have just planted out young seedlings – for the keen gardener, is a definite plus point! However, I did catch the female Muscovy pulling the heads off my snowdrops recently! My husband says I should threaten her with orange sauce but, while I'm firmly in favour of local food, I do find it hard to imagine eating something that wags its tail at you.

As we've given all our ducks names (the Balis are Dilly and Dally, and the chocolate Muscovies, Cadbury and Bendicks), they will never end up as table birds; they are primarily pets. However, eating the eggs is another matter, and my husband is eagerly anticipating a steady supply of duck eggs, which are larger and more strongly flavoured than those from chickens. This may cause some marital disharmony though, as I'm more of the opinion that eggs are for hatching, and would rather anticipate having a lot of ducklings around in the spring! I'm already casting speculative glances at our back lawn, which I think would divide into four good-sized duck pens. I could then have some more Balis in chocolate and blue... and, perhaps, a few of the beautiful green Cayugas that I was admiring at the National... and... •

Raising geese

Steve and Natalie Wright have been keeping geese for six years. They've learnt plenty along the way, and have lots of practical advice for those interested in getting started

Clearly geese are very different from chickens and, as such, they have distinctive requirements that need to be understood by all those who keep them. While there are many things to consider before starting with geese – and perhaps some challenges for people who may have kept only hens in the past – we should begin by establishing that geese are very resilient birds.

Obviously they are more effectively weather-proofed than hens, and also tend to live considerably longer. When it came to breed selection, we chose the largest breed we could find, the Norfolk White, as we felt they would be much better at defending themselves against predators.

The basics

The first point to appreciate is that the goose is a grazing animal. Not everyone realises this, or appreciates the sort of area needed to keep these birds happy and contented. If you're planning to have geese roaming around your garden, then you must expect that any edible plants will be destroyed! Our geese got in through an open gate one morning and before the day was done had eaten many of our patio plants and left us with a load of horrible droppings to clear up!

The droppings certainly are another important practical aspect to consider, especially if your birds are to be kept near the house and in a free-range, garden environment. The places where they most like to congregate will get covered in droppings and, while these do wash away with the rain, the quantity produced can be surprising. They're not as unsavoury as those produced by a dog, but geese certainly make up for this 'shortfall' with sheer bulk; while dogs only go once or twice a day, geese produce droppings around 50 times a day. Our geese tend to spend a lot of time milling around at the gate, close to the drive. Fortunately this area is Tarmac so it's not too difficult to wash and sweep away the inevitable build-up of droppings here.

We keep the geese in a paddock which is about an acre in size. Typically, our flock consists of about five long-term adults and ten or more birds which are being grown for the table. There's a stream which runs down one side of the paddock and the geese love to use this. At night, they're shut away in a fox-proof enclosure. Sometimes the paddock is also occupied by horses and ponies but, thankfully, they and the geese seem to get along perfectly well.

Food and water

As well as grazing grass, geese seem to benefit from a regular ration of poultry layers pellets. We treat-feed our chickens all sorts of vegetable waste, including cooked

It can be fun to have young geese in the garden, and entertaining for young children. However, as the birds get bigger, so do their droppings!

This big bucket of water is perfect for geese, and they do appreciate it when it's cleaned and filled.

bread. However, we've found that the geese are much more selective about what they eat than the hens. They love bread and will devour it as if they haven't eaten anything for days. They also like apples, pumpkins and squash. However, from experience, we generally find everything else is best given to the hens.

When it comes to drinking, we simply use large horse drinkers or buckets. The geese love to dip their heads into water and wash their faces. We understand that it's important for them to do this regularly to keep their eyes clean and healthy, so using a typical chicken-type drinker wouldn't be appropriate for geese. Our geese are particularly lucky to have regular access to the stream, where they enjoy a good splash around whenever they like. We did also build a pond for them in their enclosure. It's important, however, to realise that their claws can easily puncture the typical sort of rubber liner sheeting, and that any standing water like this will need to be cleaned out regularly and without fail.

The birds' drinking water containers also require regular cleaning – another important welfare-related issue. For some reason, we've noticed that they like to take a beak-full of pellets then

swish their heads around in a bucket of water with their beaks half open! To counter this wasteful behaviour we tried relocating the feeding points a long way away from the water, but this didn't make any difference at all. As a consequence of this, if the water isn't changed regularly, it'll soon start to smell and accumulate a layer of sludge at the bottom of the bucket. Obviously we don't want to put anyone off at this early stage, but it's important to appreciate that geese do require a different sort of maintenance routine from chickens.

Fly away Peter!

Geese are fliers so, if you don't want them to fly away, then you'll need to clip their wings. Ideally, this will need to be done twice a year. While chickens can only fly or flutter short distances, most ducks and geese are much more proficient, and will happily fly a long way given the chance. One day I noticed that one of our geese was missing and feared the worst, assuming that it had been taken by a fox. However, later that week we spotted the missing bird among a bank of swans on the nearby river. That was five years ago and I'm happy to report that it's still there to this day!

We have found wing-clipping

easy enough. You can get some special scissors for the job, or just use a very strong pair of normal ones. Since they all look the same, we round all the geese up into a stable and release one at a time back into the field once the wings are clipped. You only need to do one wing, and should cut the feathers down to the tips of the second line of feathers on the underside of the wing. This job can be done with just one person but, like many things, it's certainly easier with two. Some keepers prefer to tackle the job sitting down, but it's largely a matter of experience.

Geese and children

Any newly-hatched or young birds will tend to be adored by young children, and geese are no exception in this respect. However, you should always be careful when handling the young birds, especially with toddlers. You don't want them to get scratched or covered in droppings. If you hold the bird firmly around the legs and with its bottom facing away from you, any droppings produce will fall harmlessly to the ground instead of down you or your child! It's definitely fun to see young birds outside your back door, dashing around and eating the grass in your

Wing clipping is a simple job. The primary feathers of one wing should be cut back to a length matching the second row of feathers, on the underside of the wing.

Geese only really need access to a bucket of water, but they do enjoy use of a pond if you are prepared to make them one. This simple, elevated pond was designed for ease of cleaning – which is an important, practical consideration since it needs to be done regularly.

garden before they need moving into their own quarters.

But it's important to make sure that you don't keep geese in a garden environment for too long. As well as destroying your plants and leaving ever-larger droppings around the place, you may also find that while one week the children are chasing the geese, the next week the geese – being a little older and bigger – may start chasing the children.

Young children are easily frightened by adult geese. The geese are territorial creatures, and noisy too when they feel their space is being invaded. If children (or adults, for that matter) run away from the geese, the birds are likely to give chase. So it's important that larger children and adults learn to stand their ground or, better still, walk towards the geese with arms spread; they need to know who is the boss. Best of all is to work on establishing a good relationship between you, your

children and your geese. You can help with this by remembering to take some old bread with you when you are visiting, or just passing by. Geese will learn to recognise their owners, and will certainly be far less challenging if you're the ones giving them their favourite gastronomic delight. Yes, it's amazing how popular stale bread can be!

Growing for the table

When we first got our geese they came from S&T Poultry (tel: 07885 718195, or visit the website at: www.sandtpoultry.co.uk), together with a delivery of Guinea fowl. They were supplied as week-old youngsters, and so needed to be fed on chick crumb, with constant access to clean, fresh drinking water and a heat source.

If you're growing birds purely for the table, it's important to plan ahead for the time when you want them to be ready. While it's possible to grow chickens for the table in six

to 12 weeks, geese tend to be grown for 20 weeks, and sometimes longer. Also, these birds don't tend to get tough in their first year, so can make good eating for quite some time. Some of you may have heard keepers referring to a 'green goose'. This is a bird that's been slaughtered early; typically at around the 16-week-old mark. Obviously these are smaller birds and have less fat, but they remain very tasty nonetheless.

Given that geese are grazing birds, you may want to build into your growing plans the timing of the traditionally, protein-rich periods of grass growth. If you're familiar with native ponies, you may know that this is a time when grazing for such animals needs to be restricted to prevent laminitis. The key period is the spring season from late March, when the grass begins to grow rich and strong after the winter slow down has passed. The days are lengthening at this time, and the combination of sun and rain with milder temperatures leads to very good grass for geese, with a protein content of up to 14%. This means that they will naturally consume less of what seems to be increasingly expensive pellet feed. In September there tends to be another spurt of growth but there is less protein in the grass at this time of year. Sheep and geese grazed together can work very well, by the way. The sheep eat the rougher grass that the geese don't like, leaving perfect sward for the geese to pick at. •

Hatching and rearing:
Questions and answers

PREPARATION

Where do I get hatching eggs?

Q I've been trying to buy some eggs for hatching, but I'm finding it quite difficult to get them from breeders. Having tried several people in breeder's directories, the message coming back is that nobody has any available.

Can you help with some advice about suppliers or people who would sell me some hatching eggs? I've never hatched eggs before, and have bought a small incubator from eBay and just can't wait to try it out!

A The reason you're finding it so difficult to source hatching eggs could be because it's the wrong time of year. Most poultry keepers don't hatch during the winter months as fertility tends to be low, and there's also the problem of rearing chicks during the cold months.

You didn't mention the breeds you were trying to buy, so we're guessing they are pure breeds which poses another problem. These birds simply aren't laying at this time of year – some may even still be in the moult – so stocks of fertile eggs are bound to be virtually non-existent.

However, if you do manage to find someone to supply you with eggs, be very careful as there's a distinct possibility that they'll not hatch anyway, and you'll have wasted your money. On the other hand, you may be lucky and have some hatching success, in which case do make sure that you have adequate facilities for brooding and rearing the resultant chicks during the winter. Supplementary heat for the young birds is absolutely essential.

Egg washing

Q Can you tell me what is safe to clean my eggs with, as I have been told that they have to be cleaned before I put them into my incubator? Also, I have about ten eggs and my incubator is designed to hold 20, so is it OK just to put in the ten eggs? I do not have the room in my garden for any more than the ten birds.

A The inside of an incubator is a perfect place for any form of bacterial infection to thrive, so keeping the interior as clean as possible is very important.

There are several egg washes on the market which are recommended for cleaning the eggs and these normally come in the form of a powder which is diluted in water and you then wash the eggs in the mixed solution.

One product that I find extremely good for the cleaning is 'Milton'. This is the product used for cleaning and sanatising babies' bottles, and so is totally safe for both you and the eggs.

When cleaning, handle the eggs carefully, trying not to shake or knock them. Scrape off the excess dirt with a knife or a small hand scrubbing brush then, to sanitise, use luke warm water and dip the egg into a cleaning solution and wipe clean. It is not a good idea to just put the eggs into the water and let them sit there for any length of time because the egg shell is porous and can absorb the cleaning fluid. Once the egg is clean, allow it to dry naturally and then give them time to stand before putting them into the incubator.

With regards to the ten eggs into a 20-egg incubator this will cause you no problems, as you do not need to fill the incubator to

capacity for it to work correctly. What you must take into consideration is that not all the eggs will be fertile and even if they are fertile not all will survive the incubation process and hatch.

Sitting

Q I am new to keeping chickens and I want to hatch some chicks of my own. I have a hen which has gone broody and my friend has offered to give me some eggs for the hen to sit on. I am not allowed to keep a cockerel because of where I live, so this gives me my first opportunity to experience hatching some chicks. My question is; how many eggs can I put under my hen? She is a Silkie cross which I am told are the best hens for raising and hatching chicks.

A Your first consideration is that when you hatch the chicks it is inevitable that there will be some male chicks (cockerels) in the hatch, for it is almost impossible to hatch 100% hens (but not unknown). This means that if you are not allowed to keep the males then you need to know how and where you can dispose of the unwanted birds. This can be a problem, as there is no demand for cockerels. If you are prepared to grow the birds on and cull for the table, growing chicks on will also allow you to cull the cocks as they become vocal and begin to crow.

There is the other option of culling them while they are young, though most breeds need to be grown on until at least ten weeks before you can sex them. You can cull at hatch day if you are using an Auto-sexing breed which are sexed by colour as they hatch. Silkie x Sussex are a good example as these provide White/silver males and Brown/Buff females, other auto sex breeds include Plymouth Rock x Rhode Island Red which give gold female and silver/white males, Plymouth Rocks can also be crossed with many breeds to produce this sex linked offspring. Rhode Island

Red x Sussex is a very old favourite that gives the same result: Gold Female – Silver Male.

Wellbar and Cream legbar also originate from these crosses and are increasingly more popular due to their origin that includes the Wellsummer; this gives the very dark brown egg which is always in demand.

As regards to how many eggs can be set under the broody hen depends on the size of the bird. Normally a sitting of eggs varies, but this is normally around 8/10 for your bird, although I have known other larger breeds to sit and successfully hatch as many as 16, but that is very unusual. I would let her sit the amount I have recommended and I am sure that this will give you a good hatch result.

In the future you may want to hatch some different breeds. This can then vary the number of eggs you can set under the hen – the amount of eggs she can accommodate will depend on the actual size of the egg itself. If the eggs are very small bantam eggs then you may be able to add one

or two extra to the clutch of eggs that you want her to sit, but if you want to try and hatch some from a larger breed then this will mean letting her sit and cover a smaller number of eggs due to their much larger size.

Fertility check

Q I have a question about checking to see if my eggs are likely to hatch and I have been told that you should check the eggs while they are under the hen. Can you explain how I do this and at what time during the sitting period is the best?

A Checking eggs for fertility is called 'candling' and this is as the name suggests: you hold a candling lamp to one end of the egg and this enables you to see through the shell and check out the inside for signs of life.

If you are new to this process I suggest you check the eggs at around 12 days, as there will be development inside the egg that is easily seen. This can be done at an

PREPARATION

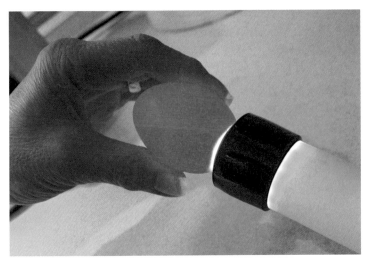

earlier date but to the inexperienced eye there may not be enough to determine whether or not the egg is fertile.

What you will see is best described as a black dot which extends into what appears to be a sort of spider's web. This is the chick embryo starting to develop and as time goes on this becomes a more solid mass which fills the inside of the egg leaving a space at one end which is the air sac from which the chick breaths, but this is much further on in the incubation period.

When you do candle the eggs remove just a few at a time from under the hen as if you disturb her too much the stress may make her walk away and leave the eggs. If you have any eggs whose fertility you're not quite sure of, then mark them so that they can be checked again in a few days time (infertile eggs will look 'opaque' when the light is shone through the shell).

These infertile eggs need to be removed as they go addled and can explode which not only smells terrible but also spreads disease and can infect the other eggs.

Marking eggs

Q I only have a few birds and I have decided to increase my flock by hatching some of my own. I collect two or three eggs

each day but I need about 20 to 25 to be able to fill my incubator.

Is it a good idea to put them into the incubator as I collect them or am I better to put the eggs in all at once? If I save them, how long can I keep the eggs before I put them in an incubator before they become infertile?

A When you incubate eggs it is very important that the eggs that are going to be set in the incubator are as fresh as possible. The older the egg becomes the

lower the fertility rate and the less chance of successful hatching.

You describe two to three eggs per day, which means that you have to save the eggs between seven and eight days. This will be no problem provided that you store the eggs correctly and turn them on a daily basis. I would suggest that as you collect your eggs you just mark them with a pencil to show the date collected; this will give you an accurate record of the egg's age, which bird laid it, and will let you know which of your birds are fertile and which are not.

The eggs need to be stored carefully in an environment that has a stable temperature. Use a normal egg tray and raise one end slightly as this then allows you to tilt the eggs gently one way and then the other on a daily basis. By doing this you are preventing the embryos from sticking to the side of the egg. Turning while in storage needs to be only slight and not to the extent that the incubator turns the eggs.

Egg mixing

Q I have recently bought a Hovabator incubator which is an automatic turning model; it has a tray which holds about 50 eggs. I have both bantam and large chickens and want to incubate some eggs of both sizes, is it possible to put the eggs into the incubator together or do I need to separate them? The eggs from both size chickens fit into the holder in the tray as I have tried that already.

A The Hovabator is a very good choice and is an ideal first incubator, plus buying the automatic one is a very wise decision. They normally hold 42 eggs and are suitable for most sizes of chicken eggs.

The answer to your question is yes, you can mix the sizes of eggs in the incubator – they will hatch as normal and as long as they are all chickens the incubation time will be the same regardless of size.

The time you may meet a

problem is after the chicks have hatched and it is time for you to move the chicks into the brooder.

The first few days should not be a problem but it does not take long for the chicks to grow and develop and this is when the larger chicks can become a danger to the smaller chicks in the brooder. It is just a matter of who is the heaviest, for if huddled into a corner the small ones can be trodden and suffocated. The best way to combat this problem is to move the chicks by size into two separate brooders to avoid any fatalities.

Incubator cleaning

Q I'm getting excited about the prospect of hatching my first birds this year, and will be using an incubator which belonged to my brother. It's a unit called a Hovabator, and is a hand-turn machine. It certainly needs a good clean, and to be properly set-up before I can use it.

I'd be very grateful for any practical advice you have about this.

A The Hovabator is an old design of incubator that was built in America. From your description we imagine that you

have one the basic, manual model, and the good news is that these are the easiest to operate.

With regard to the cleaning, the first thing to bear in mind is that these machines are made primarily from polystyrene, and all the electrical fittings are built into the lid. Inside the unit, the eggs sit in a plastic tray and are covered with protective mesh.

Take the unit apart and wash everything except the inside of the lid, where the electrical components are fitted. Use a good quality disinfectant such as Barrier V1 or Virkon, then just give everything plenty of time to dry. As a back-up, just before you set the eggs, lightly spray them with a

suitable incubator/hatching disinfectant.

The lid of the unit requires more care as, amongst other things, it houses the important sensor and thermostat units. Try cleaning around the most delicate parts using a soft brush; you'll mainly be removing dust from the inside of the lid. If you want to use a cleaning product too, then spray it on to a cloth first and use that to wipe the areas being cleaned.

When you're satisfied that everything's adequately clean, plug the unit into the mains and give it time to warm up. Wait until it reaches its operating temperature (37.5-37.8°C, depending on your preference), then leave it for a couple of hours to be sure that this temperature is being maintained consistently. If a small adjustment is required, use the metal lever on top of the unit, once its locking nut has been loosened. You'll only need to move this very slightly, then wait at least an hour for things to settle down again before re-checking the new temperature.

The important thing to be sure of is that the machine is running consistently with regard to internal temperature. Once stable, leave it to run for 24 hours to make finally sure that all's well, then you're ready to set the eggs.

INCUBATOR USEAGE

Incubator settings

Q We are very new to incubation and we are a little confused. We are being told several different temperatures' settings for our incubator. It is only a small 50-egg model which has a plastic top and is automatic. Can you give me the correct setting please?

A This is a very common question and there are certain manufacturers who recommend temperatures of 35°C and yet another may say 36°C or 37°C – and then you have the incubators that are in Fahrenheit which tell you 99°F!

I have always used 37.5°C to 37.8°C in all my incubators that have varied from the smaller Fiem to the very large Marseilles and I have had excellent results. The slight variation depends on the user, though I personally prefer the 37.8°C as this gives me the best results.

The outcome will also depend on where the incubator is situated as it needs to be in a place where the temperature is stable with no

excessive heat changes caused by draught, direct sunlight or central heating etc.

When you set the incubator make sure you allow it to run to the set temperature for at least 24 hours to enable you to get the correct reading and then you can add the eggs.

Please note this setting is for chickens – other species can vary.

Humidity

Q I keep reading about the humidity inside the incubator. I have had quite a few chicks that have hatched under my Silkie X broody hen but I really fancy the challenge of hatching some chicks in an incubator. However, it looks a little complicated – can you explain what I need to do as regards the settings of an incubator?

A The settings on any incubator are basically the temperature and the humidity. The temperature represents the heat at which the chicks can develop and grow and eventually hatch. The humidity is the amount of water that is inside the egg as it develops.

The temperature needs to be set at 37.5°C to 37.8°C. The incubators are normally pre set by the manufacturer but if adjustments are needed then this is done by slightly turning an adjuster screw on the incubator. You will only need the slightest turn to alter the setting and then the incubator needs to be left for the temperature to re-adjust itself to the new setting. This adjustment will take a little time and you have to be patient, but once set that is all you need to do unless the adjustment is tampered with. The reading is from the thermometer, which is normally set inside the incubator where you can see it quite easily.

Humidity is the amount of water needed to allow the chicks to hatch. Too much water and they drown, too little water and the shell becomes very hard and they cannot break out to hatch.

The ideal settings are for the incubator humidity to run at 35/45°C for the first 10/15 days and then increase this setting up to 55/70°C for the final days and into hatch day. This all depends on where the incubator is situated, but all incubators need to be in an area where the temperature remains the same day and night with no large temperature rises or falls.

Humidity boost

Q I am putting my eggs into the incubator and I read that you add water into the tray in the bottom; at what stage do I add the water and is it OK if I use tap water or is there a special water to use inside the incubator?

A The amount of water and when to add the water is very dependent on where you have your incubator situated and just how stable the environment is around the incubator.

I never add water until around day 15 as the outside humidity is normally around 35°C during many months of the year. By adding water you increase the humidity and in some cases this makes the water content in the egg far too high during the early stages of incubation.

If you have the incubator in a suitable place where the outside humidity is reading 35/45°C then

Hatching and rearing: **Questions and answers**

water should not be needed until nearer the time for hatching. Most incubators are used in the home, which is normally quite a dry environment, so add small amounts of water at a time until you achieve the required 35/45°C reading. Many incubators do not include a humidity gauge but they are essential to allow you to judge the humidity both outside and inside the incubator.

Humidity gauges come in various forms from a basic dial type, similar to the ones used in greenhouses and reasonably cheap to buy, or you can use the electronic sensor gauges, though these can range widely in prices depending on how sophisticated they. Check with your local poultry supply company or incubator seller, which I am sure will be able to supply you with what you need.

With regards to the use of tap water, this varies from county to county. Some water is classed as soft and some is very hard. Most incubator manufacturers recommend the use of distilled water, and that is possibly the safest and the best way to keep your incubator in perfect condition.

I have used tap water for many years in my own incubator without any problems but I make sure I clean it thoroughly each and every time I use the machine. You can see

that the water leaves various deposits but if they are kept clean and not allowed to build up then there is no reason why tap water cannot be used.

Life in the incubator

Q My chicks are due to hatch within a few days. They are in an automatic incubator which, according to the manufacturer, can also be used for hatching.

(1) Do I need to turn off the egg turner?

(2) When they hatch, how long can I leave them in there and when do I start to feed them?

(3) I know I have to move them into a brooder under a lamp, but what is the temperature got to be in the brooder and how do I check that?

A Modern incubators can be used as both incubators and hatchers, they work very well and in most cases the cabinet type of incubator comes with a hatching tray in the base of the unit as standard.

(1) Turning off the turner motor needs to done at day 19/20 and, if removable, take it away. Alternatively, if there is a hatching tray move the eggs into the tray ready for hatching. By removing the turner you help to protect the chicks from becoming trapped or injured.

(2) Once the chicks hatch you need to leave them in the incubator for up to 36 hours; this gives them time to fluff up and also time for the later arrivals to hatch. Do not feed them in the incubator as they have enough stored in there own yolk sack to keep them fed for this period. Also, feeding them inside the incubator will only lead to infection and disease caused by the wasted food.

INCUBATOR USEAGE & BROODING

(3) As soon as the chicks dry out and become fluffy, move them into the brooder, set the heat lamp at approx the same setting as the incubator for the first day then reduce to around 32°C, making sure the chicks are well spread out and not huddled together in the middle of the brooder. If they are, this shows they are to cold. I check this by laying a thermometer directly under the light on the floor and once set I remove the thermometer and watch the chicks reaction – they will soon tell you that they are either too hot or too cold.

Incubation records

Q I understand that chickens take 21 days to hatch but when I do count the days from? Do I count these days from the first day I put the eggs into the incubator?

Also, when the chicks are hatching, how many days past the 21 can be allowed in case of some hatching late?

A Hatching chickens takes a 21-day period, once you have set your incubator. The unit needs to be operating for at least 24 hours to make sure it is stable and running correctly, and then you add the eggs. In all cases you open the incubator while you are setting the eggs and this means that the temperature and humidity are lost for a short period, so this needs to be rebuilt as soon as the incubator is closed and sealed. Once the eggs are set, make a note on your calendar or even create a simple incubator chart to give you a record of all that happens during this 21 day period.

The start day for that 21 days needs to be from next day 24 hours later – this gives the eggs time to reach the correct temperature and by using this date you can work out the hatch day from that time on the calendar.

Helping to hatch

Q I have recently hatched my first chicks in an incubator. I am new to this, and I discovered that some of the chicks were having difficulty getting out of the egg. Most of the chicks hatched perfectly but some seemed as though they were not strong enough to be able to break out.

I did not know what to do and I wondered if it is possible to help them get free. The chicks had in some cases made holes and some had started to cut round the egg but that was as far as it seemed they could go.

The problem I had was that my young daughter was upset because she could hear the chicks making a noise from inside the shell.

Can I help to get these birds free in the future without doing any damage and will they survive? Is there anyway of telling before this time if they will not hatch? Any advice would be appreciated.

A Assisted hatching is a topic that has long caused controversy; it is always a problem to decide whether we help

INCUBATOR RECORD CARD

Date egg set	1st day start	Hatch date	Number of eggs	Egg type	Outside Temp	Room Temp	Incubator Temp	Humidity	Notes
01/01/09	02/01/09	23/01/09	24	Sussex	30°	35°	37.5°	45%	

a struggling chick at this time or leave nature to take its own course.

The belief is that if the bird cannot exit the egg normally then the result may be birds of poor quality that are weak and have a very low survival rate.

Be aware that in some case the chicks must be given time to hatch normally – not all chicks hatch on the same day and, in some cases, they may even be one or two days late. So always allow for these slight variation in time especially if the eggs in the incubator are a variety of eggs collected at different times. The older the egg the more likely it is that it may take a little longer to hatch.

Helping the chick out of the shell is not for the faint-hearted, as there is a possibility that the chick will not have developed fully and will still have the yolk sack on the outside of the body. If this is the case then the chick will more than likely die and also there is a possible that it will bleed to death as you attempt to break the shell to assist the hatch. The timing has to be perfect to be able to get the chick out of the shell without causing any ill effects to the hatching chick.

Once you have started to help the bird to hatch there is virtually no chance of turning back, but as soon as you start to remove the shell the signs will show almost immediately as to whether you have made the right or wrong decision. If the blood appears as you start to remove the shell then this shows that it is too early to attempt to release the chick, but at this stage the signs of blood will in most cases show you that it is too late and the damage is done, this will in almost all cases result in the loss of the chick.

I do realize that when the chick can be heard inside the shell it is very disturbing and makes it tempting to try and help. Never try to help unless the chick has actually broken through and can be seen moving.

If the shell is completely closed do not attempt to go into the egg, as the chick will not survive.

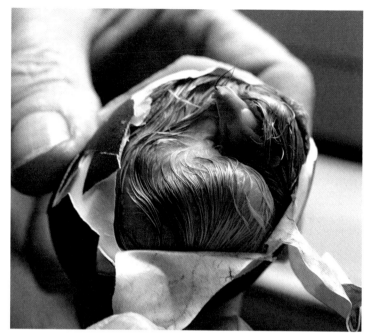

If the chick has broken through and has what is called 'piped' then if you really want to try and help the bird then just remove the smallest possible piece of shell and make sure there are no signs of blood. If this is clear carry on, but only the very tiniest pieces are to be removed.

It is a good idea to dampen the shell with luke warm water to try and soften the inner membrane, for the membrane does dry and becomes similar to a tough thin rubber which makes it very difficult for the chick to hatch. The effort required causes the chick to become weak with no strength left to break clear of the egg. In fact, the lack of humidity can be a cause of the hatching problem so to help avoid this increase the humidity in the incubator a few days before the hatch date. The higher humidity will help to keep the membrane moist and prevent it from drying out.

During this time try to be patient and if the chick can be successfully removed then place it in a warm brooder and allow it to dry naturally and regain its strength.

Assisted hatched chicks are better if placed in a separate brooder from the ones who have hatch normally and have already had the time for gaining in strength. Leave them alone and allow them to get over the stress of the hatch, making sure they drink and, once standing, they can be fed.

I do believe that the success rate for assisted hatching is very low, and unless you are almost certain that the bird is ready and capable of hatching with the result being a healthy good quality chick then it is better left in its shell with Mother Nature being allowed to take her course.

Losing chicks

Q I have over 30 chicks in my brooder, but I have lost 19 chicks of various breeds, mostly Silkies and some Faverolles. There appears to be nothing wrong with them as far as I can see but obviously there is. They do not have mite or dirty vents and seemed perfectly healthy one day but dead by the next morning. Have you any idea as to the cause or any suggestions? The chicks are from two to five weeks old.

I feel so helpless when all I can do is stand by and wait for them to die.

INCUBATOR USEAGE & BROODING

A There are several reasons that may be causing these losses, one of the main ones being that there is an infection inside the brooder, this could be caused by damp and soiled bedding which, when warm, creates many problems both internal and respiratory. One of the main killers of chicks is Coccidiosis, a worm that attacks the internal organs of the chick causing serious internal damage, and this is both contagious and fatal in most cases. I suggest you completely clean the brooder and use a powder disinfectant such as Stalosan – put this under the bedding and this will disinfect and dry out the damp infected areas, then put the shavings on top and keep checking and removing damp patches. I would also make sure that the brooder is large enough to house the chicks and also make sure that this is adequate for them as they grow. Overcrowding in the brooder is one of the main causes of Coccidiosis.

If Coccidiosis is found you will need to contact a vet for treatment, which will be a prescription-only medicine. This is normally administered by adding the treatment to the water and I would treat all chicks in the future even before the problem shows itself, as if this is Coccidiosis then it lives in the brooder for many months even when the brooder is not in use. Thoroughly clean and disinfect before you use the same brooder for a fresh batch of chicks. Signs of the disease can be blood in the droppings (easily seen on clean shavings), but there are some strains which unfortunately do not show signs, only that the chicks become droopy and lethargic.

If the chicks were suffering from a respiratory disease you would see signs of breathing difficulties and sneezing. Eyes closed and runny noses are also signs that there is a serious problem that needs to be treated. Again, cleanliness and dryness are essential and the vet will need to prescribe a suitable treatment for these problems.

You also mention two breeds, one of which is the Silkie. This could be another possible cause of your problems as most Silkie chickens are vaccinated against Meraks, a disease from which they are prone to suffer. If they are not vaccinated they will in most cases die and may also infect the other chicks in the brooder. You really have to be careful that you do not mix breeds that are normally vaccinated with breeds that are non-vaccinated as this can lead to some very serious infections and in most cases many fatalities.

Heat, food and water

Q When I move the chicks into my brooder that I have made myself with a heat lamp that hangs above the box, how long do I need to keep the chicks under the heat? Plus do I feed and water them as soon as they are put into the brooder?

A The chicks are under the heat for as long as is necessary for them to mature and feather enough to allow them to stand the normal outside temperatures. This varies depending on the time of the year but as a general rule they are in the brooder for around six to seven weeks. This is a rough guide; some breeds need longer than others. Chicks that are removed from the heat will soon give signs of discomfort and cold (chirping and huddling together are usual signs of being unhappy).

Moving the chicks from the incubator to the brooder needs to be done as quickly as possible, to avoid stress and also to prevent the chicks from becoming chilled. The brooder needs to be set close to equivalent temperature to the incubator (37.5°C) for the first day and then can be lowered gradually as the chicks grow and strengthen, this is easily achieved by watching the reaction of the chicks – if they are too warm they will spread out into a wide circle, if they are too cold they will huddle together under the heat lamp. The ideal situation is for them to be moving around, quite active and evenly spread.

You need to add both food and water from day one. I advise that you use a very narrow lipped chick drinker which is also shallow, this is to prevent accidents from drowning because chicks will go back to water as soon as they hatch and they will drown if not protected.

Feed needs to be in the form of chick crumbs which are purchased from your local feed merchant. I always set the chicks in the brooder and then sprinkle the feed using my hand from about 4ins above the bedding into the brooder, this gets the chicks interested and starts them to peck and feed. Use a small chick feeder, making sure there are no places were the chicks can come to any harm. The solid type of feeder is better as there is no access to the inside where the chicks can become trapped. •